FIRST MULTICOLOUR EDITION

The Language of Chemistry OR Chemical Equations

and how to master them

Including Balancing of Equations

- *By Ion-Electron Method*
- *By Oxidation Number Method*

G.D. TULI
Ex-Principal
Shyamlal College
Delhi University, Delhi

P.L. SONI
Formerly, Head of the Deptt. of Chemistry
Hans Raj College
Delhi University, Delhi

EPH
Eurasia Publishing House

EPH
Eurasia Publishing House

S. CHAND SCHOOL BOOKS
(An imprint of S. Chand Publishing)
A Division of S. Chand & Co. Pvt. Ltd.
7361, Ram Nagar, Qutab Road, New Delhi-110055
Phone: 23672080-81-82, 9899107446, 9911310888; Fax: 91-11-23677446
www.schandpublishing.com; e-mail : helpdesk@schandpublishing.com

Branches :

Ahmedabad	:	Ph: 27541965, 27542369, ahmedabad@schandgroup.com
Bengaluru	:	Ph: 22268048, 22354008, bangalore@schandgroup.com
Bhopal	:	Ph: 4274723, 4209587, bhopal@schandgroup.com
Chandigarh	:	Ph: 2725443, 2725446, chandigarh@schandgroup.com
Chennai	:	Ph. 28410027, 28410058, chennai@schandgroup.com
Coimbatore	:	Ph: 2323620, 4217136, coimbatore@schandgroup.com (Marketing Office)
Cuttack	:	Ph: 2332580; 2332581, cuttack@schandgroup.com
Dehradun	:	Ph: 2711101, 2710861, dehradun@schandgroup.com
Guwahati	:	Ph: 2738811, 2735640, guwahati@schandgroup.com
Haldwani	:	Mob. 09452294584 (Marketing Office)
Hyderabad	:	Ph: 27550194, 27550195, hyderabad@schandgroup.com
Jaipur	:	Ph: 2219175, 2219176, jaipur@schandgroup.com
Jalandhar	:	Ph: 2401630, 5000630, jalandhar@schandgroup.com
Kochi	:	Ph: 2378740, 2378207-08, cochin@schandgroup.com
Kolkata	:	Ph: 22367459, 22373914, kolkata@schandgroup.com
Lucknow	:	Ph: 4076971, 4026791, 4065646, 4027188, lucknow@schandgroup.com
Mumbai	:	Ph: 22690881, 22610885, mumbai@schandgroup.com
Nagpur	:	Ph: 2720523, 2777666, nagpur@schandgroup.com
Patna	:	Ph: 2300489, 2302100, patna@schandgroup.com
Pune	:	Ph: 64017298, pune@schandgroup.com
Raipur	:	Ph: 2443142, Mb. : 09981200834, raipur@schandgroup.com (Marketing Office)
Ranchi	:	Ph: 2361178, Mob. 09430246440, ranchi@schandgroup.com
Siliguri	:	Ph: 2520750, siliguri@schandgroup.com (Marketing Office)
Visakhapatnam	:	Ph: 2782609 (M) 09440100555, visakhapatnam@schandgroup.com (Marketing Office)

First Edition 1944
Reprints 1977(Twice), 78, 79, 80, 81, 82, 83, 84, 85, 88, 89, 90, 91, 92, 93 (Twice), 96, 97, 98, 99, 2001, 2002, 2003, 2004
First Multicolour Edition 2005, Reprints 2006, 2007, 2008, 2009, 2010, 211, 2012, 2013(Twice), 2014 (Twice), 2015, 2016

ISBN : 978-81-219-2532-7 **Code :** 1004A 278

PRINTED IN INDIA
By Vikas Publishing House Pvt. Ltd., Plot 20/4, Site-IV, Industrial Area Sahibabad, Ghaziabad-201010 and Published by S. Chand & Company Pvt. Ltd., 7361, Ram Nagar, New Delhi-110055.

PREFACE TO THE TWENTY-FIRST EDITION

(First Multicolour Edition)

It gives us immense pleasure to bring out the twenty-first edition of the book in multicolour with attractive illustrations. Special attention has been paid to the following points :

- Errors of the previous editions pointed out by readers from time to time have been removed.
- Point size of the text has been increased so as to make its reading easier.
- The style of the book has been modified to suit the requirements of students.
- Now the book is in new attractive format.

We hope the readers of the book will find the book all the more useful. Suggestions for further improvement will be most welcome.

Our thanks are due to the Editorial Staff of S.Chand & Company, especially to Mr. Riyaz Baqar, for his help in conversion of the book into multicolour edition and Mr. Pradeep Kr. Joshi for Designing & Layouting of this book.

Authors

Preface to the Nineteenth Edition

A common idea prevails that when **"Language of Chemistry"** constitutes a part of Inorganic Chemistry textbooks, what is the justification of bringing out a seperate booklet? To those teachers and students of chemistry, who share this view we have to offer a word of apology.

No textbook provides a sufficient number of equations to the students for practice. Moreover, the equations given are always written in the language of chemistry. The student simply reads these equations from the textbook and copies them. He never gets any practice in writing equations, with the result that he cannot balance them in any test. He loses interest in the subject and regards it as something beyond his reach.

In this small booklet a large number of equations are written in words and the students is required to translate them into the language of chemistry. He has to write correct formulae and then balance the equations independently. For verification of the result, he can look up the answers given at the end. Just in a week or two he learns the method of writing correct balanced equations. He feels interested in the subject and finds it quite his own.

For writing and naming of formulae the chemists prefer the Stock system of nomenclature. So modern names are introduced along with the classifical and trivial (common) names. Thus ferrous chloride is also written as iron (II) chloride, and so on.

Modern chemists prefer balancing chemical equations by Ion-electron method and oxidation number method. These two methods have been added in the present edition as two separate chapters (Chapters V and VI). We hope these will inspire the students to learn these modern methods.

The booklet will be equally useful for the students in schools as well as B.Sc. Students of different universitities.

One of the Special Features of the present edition is the inclusion of **'Test your Understanding'** at the end of each chapter. These exercises will help the student to revise the chapter as well as test his/her understanding.

The last two chapters (Chapters VII and VIII) entitled 'Test yourself on these Typical Questions' have been added for the benefit of examinees. It will enable them to test their knowledge before the examination.

We are grateful to all those who sent their suggestions for improvement of the booklet. Any suggestion for its improvement will be thankfully received.

Authors

CONTENTS

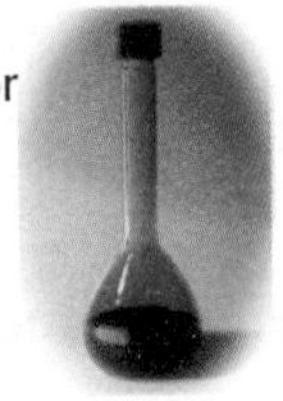

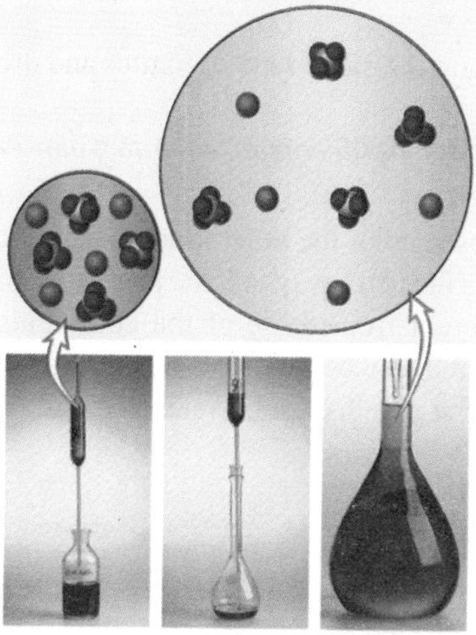

1 CHAPTER

Introduction

1. Chemistry and its Language. Every science has its own technical terms and usually it requires considerable effort on the part of a beginner to master them. Chemistry is no exception. It is full not only of technical terms but also of certain expressions like H_2O, H_2SO_4 etc., which in the language of chemistry stand for the names of certain definite chemical substances. Before we take up the study of this language, it is absolutely essential to understand some of the important technical terms which we shall come across.

2. Element. The various substances around us are of two kinds. One kind is very simple and cannot be broken up into anything simpler by any chemical method at our disposal. Substances of this kind, *e.g.*, hydrogen,

Iron (Fe) is a natural element.

Pure silver has a brilliant white metallic lustre. It is a bit harder than gold and is very ductile and malleable.

oxygen, iron, silver, etc., consist of one and the same type of matter and are called elements.

Simple forms of matter which cannot be decomposed into simpler substances are called **elements.**

3. Compound. A compound is a substance of the other kind. When two or more elements combine chemically, *i.e.*, in such a way that the properties of the resulting substance are entirely different from those of the combining elements, *a chemical compound* is obtained. It can be decomposed into simple substances by suitable chemical methods at our disposal. Water and carbon dioxide are examples of compounds.

(a) Crystalline quartz is a pure compound (SiO_2). **(b)** The red sandstone in Delicate Arch is a solid mixture of many compounds.

A compound is a substance produced by union of two or more elements in a definite proportion. It can be decomposed into two or more simple substances.

4. Atom. *The smallest particle of an element which can take part in chemical change is called an* **atom.** It may or may not be capable of independent existence.

5. Atomic Weight. Atoms are so small particles that their weights are inconveniently small in terms of grams, *i.e.*, gram is too big a unit to weigh an atom or a molecule. For example, the weight of a carbon atom is 0.000,000,000,000, 000,000,000, 0195 g (1.95×10^{-23} g). To overcome this difficulty, one-twelfth of the weight of a carbon atom (^{12}C isotope) is selected as a unit of weight for the purpose and is termed 1 atomic mass unit (1 amu).

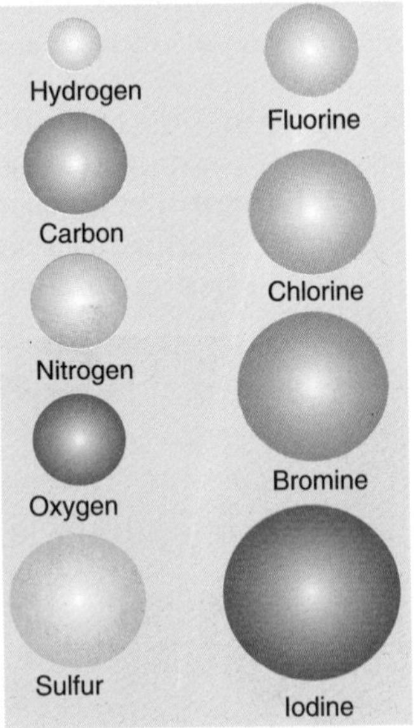

Some common atoms. The easient way to identify, atoms in pictures of models is by colour.

Atoms of the same element may have different masses. These are called isotopes. For example, chlorine has two isotopes of weights 35 amu and 37 amu. These are mixed in such a proportion that their average weight is 35.5 amu. Such an average is called atomic weight of the element.

Atomic weight *is defined as the average mass of the atoms of an element expressed in atomic mass units, carbon-12 being taken as the standard with an atomic mass of 12 amu.* By saying that atomic weight of magnesium is 24, we only mean that an atom of magnesium is twice as heavy as an atom of carbon.

6. Molecule. *The smallest particle of matter which is capable of independent existence is called a* **molecule.**

It is the smallest particle of a substance which possesses the properties of that substance. It cannot be subdivided without destroying its characteristic properties.

The molecule of an element is made up of one or more atoms of only one and the same type, while the molecule of a compound is made up of dissimilar atoms.

7. Molecular Weight. *The molecular weight of an element or a compound is defined as the relative weight of its molecule as compared with that of carbon atom (^{12}C isotope) taken as 12 amu.*

It is only a number and gives only a relative weight of the molecule. It does not give us the actual weight of the molecule at all. Molecular weight of magnesium carbonate is equal to 84 times that a molecule of magnesium carbonate is 7 times heavy as an atom of carbon or 84 times as heavy as one-twelfth of an atom of carbon.

8. Radical. The molecule of a compound is usually made up of two parts which are separately known as **radicals**. For example, the radicals present in *sodium chloride* molecule are *sodium* and *chloride* while those in potassium *nitrate are potassium and nitrate*.

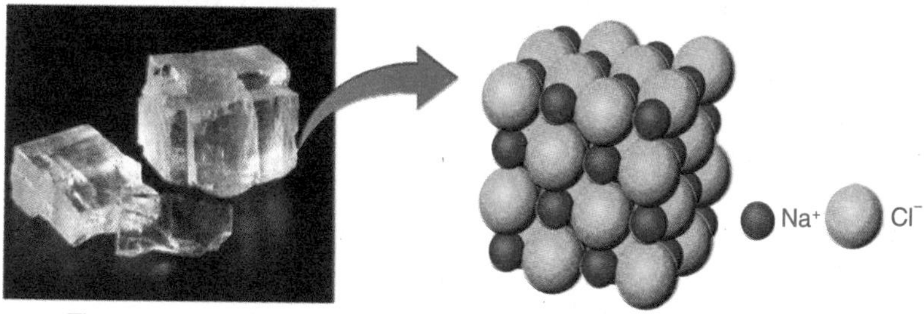

The arrangement of Na^+ ions and Cl^- ions in a crystal of sodium chloride.

Radicals are groups of atoms that react as single atoms and keep their identity in many reactions.

A radical is called a **simple radical** when it in as atom only, *e.g.*, sodium, potassium etc. It is known as a **compound radical** when it is made up of a group of two or more different atoms, *e.g., nitrate*—made up of one nitrogen atom and three oxygen atoms and sulphate–made up of one sulphur atom and four oxygen atoms. A compound radical can be introduced or expelled from combination without change.

When an acid reacts with a base, a *salt* is produced as a result of neutralization.

Sodium hydroxide + Hydrochloric acid → Sodium chloride + Water
(Base) **(Acid)** **(Salt)**

In the molecule of sodium chloride the *sodium* radical has been contributed by the base sodium hydroxide and is, therefore, called **Basic Radical**. Similarly its *chloride* radical has been contributed by hydrochloric acid and is, therefore, termed as **Acid Radical.**

In the case of inorganic salts, the metallic radicals of the type of sodium are called basic radicals while others like nitrate, sulphate and carbonate are called acid radicals. When a salt is dissolved in water, it splits up into the constituent radicals. The basic radicals then carry a positive charge (positive ions) and are, because of this reason, termed **electro-positive radicals**. The acid radicals under these circumstances carry negative charge (negative ions) and are called **electronegative radicals.**

Chlorine is a toxic green gas, sodium is a reactive metal, and sodium chloride is a harmless white solid.

TEST YOUR UNDERSTANDING

Fill in the blanks in the following :

(*i*) Simple forms of matter which cannot be decomposed into simpler substances are called.......... .

(*ii*) A ....is a substance produced by the union of two or more...........in a definite proportions. It...........be decomposed into two or more simple substances.

(*iii*) The simplest particle of an element which may or may not be capable of independent existence is termed a / an ....

(*iv*) Smallest particle of an element or a compound which is capable of .... is called a / an ....

(*v*) Atomic weight of an element is the average relative weight of its atom as compared with that of .... atom (.........isotope) taken as ....

(*vi*) Molecular weight of an .... or a .... is the relative weight of its molecule as compared with that of .... atom (......... isotope) taken as ....

(*vii*) .... are groups of atoms that react as single atoms and keep their .... in many reactions.

(*viii*) In a molecule of sodium chloride sodium is .... radical or .... radical while chloride is .... radical or .... radical.

(*ix*) Radicals carrying positive or negative charge are termed ....

KEY

(*i*) elements

(*ii*) compound, elements, can.

(*iii*) an atom.

(*iv*) independent existence, a molecule.

(*v*) Carbon, ^{12}C, 12 amu.

(*vi*) element, compound, carbon. ^{12}C, 12 amu.

(*vii*) Radicals, identity.

(*viii*) basic, electropositive, acid, electro-negative.

(*ix*) ions.

EXERCISES

I. Define the following terms and give examples :

(*i*) Element, (*ii*) Compound,

(*iii*) Atom, (*iv*) Molecule,

(*v*) Radical, (*vi*) Atomic weight,

(*vii*) Molecular weight.

II. What do you understand by the following :

(*i*) Acid radical, (*ii*) Basic radical,

(*iii*) Simple radical, (*iv*) Compound radical.

(*v*) Positive radical, and, (*vi*) Negative radical

III. Explain the statement : "Atomic weight or Molecular weight is a relative weight"

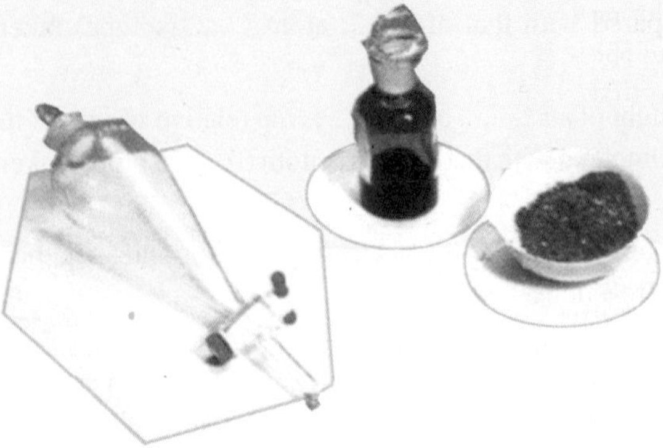

2
CHAPTER

Symbols and Formulae

1. Symbol. Just as a steno uses shorthand to save time in taking down notes from his officer, in the same manner a chemist, instead of writing full and lengthy names of elements, uses certain abbreviations called *symbols*. In the language of chemistry, a *symbol represents one atom of an element* and is usually the first letter of the name of the element. For example, O is the *symbol* for oxygen, N for nitrogen, H for hydrogen, S for sulphur and so on. When two or more elements begin with the same letter, another characteristic letter from its name is added in order to avoid confusion. Thus C stands for carbon, Ca for

A sample of calcium(Ca).

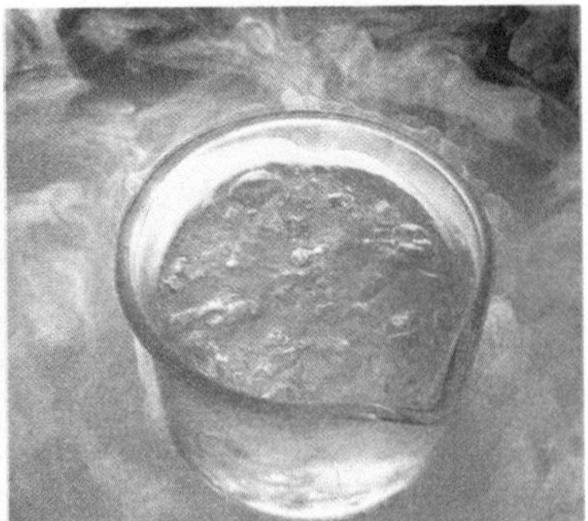

Liquid oxygen (O) has a blue colour.

calcium, Cd for cadmium, Cr for chromium, Cl for chlorine and Co for cobalt. It should be noted, however, that the first letter is always capital and the second is always small.

The abbreviations used for the lengthy names of elements are termed **symbols.**

Cobalt (Co) a bluish-gray, shiny, brittle metallic element has atomic number 27, and has magnetic properties like iron.

A symbol is not merely an abbreviation for the name of an element but has a quantitative significance as well. Thus O stands not only for the atom of oxygen but also for 16 parts by weight of it, this weight being the atomic weight of the element.

Remember. Careful attention must be paid to capital and lower case letters in the symbols. For example,

Co means the element *cobalt*

CO means the compound *carbon monoxide*

Some of the common elements with the symbols and approximate atomic weights are given in **Table I.**

Iron, though widely used as a structural materials, corrodes easily.

Samples of mercury, silver, and sulphur.

TABLE I

Element	Symbol	Approx. At. Wt.
Aluminium	Al	27
Antimony (*Stibium*)	Sb	122
Arsenic	As	75
Barium	Ba	137
Bromine	Br	80
Calcium	Ca	40
Carbon	C	12

Chlorine	Cl	35.5
Copper (*Cuprum*)	Cu	63.5
Hydrogen	H	1
Iodine	I	127
Iron (*Ferrum*)	Fe	56
Lead (*Plumbum*)	Pb	207
Magnesium	Mg	24
Mercury (*Hydrargyrum*)	Hg	201
Nitrogen	N	14
Oxygen	O	16
Phosphorus	P	31
Potassium (*Kalium*)	K	39
Silver (*Argentum*)	Ag	108
Sodium (*Natrium*)	Na	23
Sulphur	S	32
Tin (*Stannum*)	Sn	119
Zinc	Zn	65

2. Formula. Since atoms of elements combine to form molecules, it should be possible to represent the molecule in terms of symbols of the constituent atoms. *This symbolic expression for a molecule is called a* **Formula.**

A molecule of an element may contain one or more atoms of it, the number of atoms of the element present in the molecule being placed at the right lower corner of the symbol for that element. For example, H_2 represents one molecule of hydrogen containing two atoms of it, I_2 is the formula of iodine, O_2 of oxygen, N_2 of nitrogen and Cl_2 that of chlorine; $4Cl_2$ represents four molecules of chlorine.

Potassium nitrate contains one atom of potassium, one of nitrogen and three atoms of oxygen.

In case of a compound, the molecule containing different atoms united in a certain fixed ratio, is represented by placing symbols of the various elements present in it side by side indicating their number as explained above. Thus KNO_3 represents one molecule of potassium nitrate containing one atom of potassium, one of nitrogen and three atoms of oxygen ; $5CO_2$ represents five molecules of carbon dioxide, each containing one atom of carbon and two atoms of oxygen.

A formula has a quantitative or weight significance also. Thus KNO_3 represents 101 parts by weight of it containing 39 parts by weight of potassium, 14 parts by weight of nitrogen and $16 \times 3 = 48$ parts by weight of oxygen. Looking at a formula, we at once understand the ratio in which the various atoms are united to form the molecule, which the formula represents.

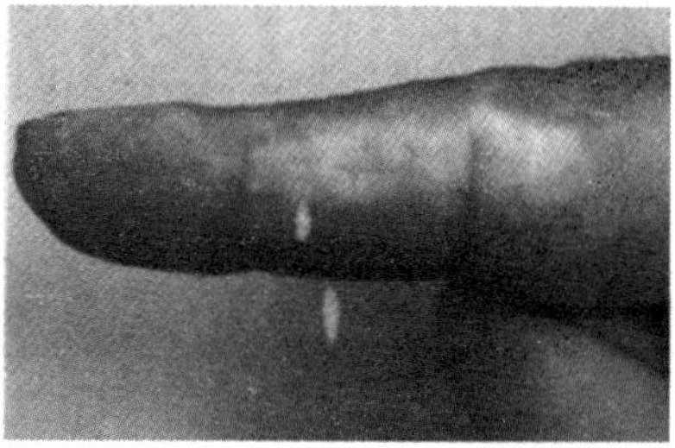
Finger stained yellow by nitric acid, (HNO_3)

3. Formulae of Some Commoner Compounds. The students will do well to commit to memory the formulae of some common compounds given **Table II.**

TABLE II

Compound	Formula	Compound	Formula
Hydrochloric acid	HCl	Silica (sand)	SiO_2
Sulphuric acid	H_2SO_4	Caustic soda	$NaOH$
Sulphurous acid	H_2SO_3	(*Sodium hydroxide*)	
Nitric acid	HNO_3	Caustic potash	KOH
Nitrous acid	HNO_2	(*Potassium hydroxide*)	
Phosphoric acid	H_3PO_4	Washing soda	Na_2CO_3
Boric acid	H_3BO_3	(*Sodium carbonate*)	
Sulphur dioxide	SO_2	Baking soda	$NaHCO_3$
Sulphur trioxide	SO_3	(*Sodium bicarbonate*)	
Nitrous oxide	N_2O	Limestone or marble	$CaCO_3$
Nitric oxide	NO	(*Calcium carbonate*)	
Nitrogen trioxide	N_2O_3	Water	H_2O
Nitrogen dioxide	NO_2	Sulphuretted hydrogen	H_2S
Nitrogen pentoxide	N_2O_5	Ammonia	NH_3
Carbon monoxide	CO	Phosphine	PH_3
Carbon dioxide	CO_2	Methane	CH_4

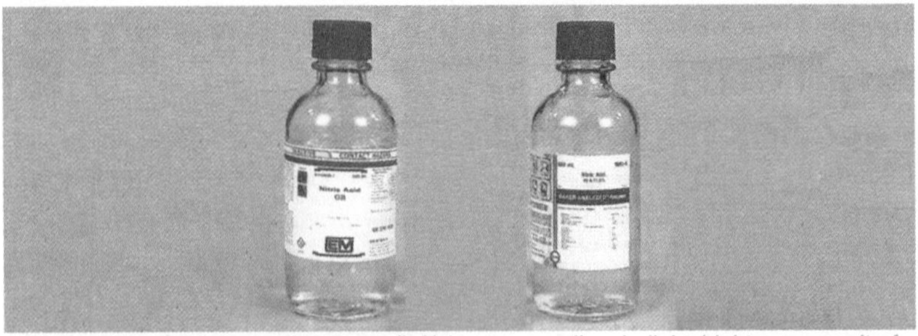

Nitric acid is colourless when pure (left) but turns yellow in light (right as a result of the formation of NO_2. Nitrogen dioxide gas is red-brown but dilute solutions look yellow.

4. Valency. Consider the following molecules :

HCl —Hydrogen chloride *(Hydrochloric acid)*

H_2O —Hydrogen oxide *(Water)*

NH_3 —Hydrogen nitride *(Ammonia)*

CH_4 —Hydrogen carbide *(Methane)*

Looking at these molecules, we find that while one chlorine atom combines with only one hydrogen atom, one oxygen atom combines with two, one nitrogen atom combines with three while one carbon atom combines with four hydrogen atoms, *i.e.*, the atoms of chlorine, oxygen, nitrogen and carbon show different combining capacities.

These samples of sulphur and carbon both contain the same number of atoms.

This combining capacity of an atom or a radical is called its ***valency****. It is measured in terms of hydrogen atoms or oxygen atoms. Valency of an atom or a radical is the number of hydrogen atoms or double the number of oxygen atoms which will combine with it.*

Iron reacting with chlorine to form iron (III) chloride ($FeCl_3$).

From the above formulae, valencies of chlorine, oxygen, nitrogen and carbon are 1, 2, 3 and 4 respectively. Similarly from the formulae CO_2 and SO_3, valencies of carbon and sulphur are 4 and 6 respectively.

5. Elements with Variable Valency. Elements like iron, mercury, copper and tin are fickle enough to have more than one valency number. In these cases, the radical with lower valency is designated by–*ous*, while one with higher valency by–*ic*. For example :

$FeCl_2$ is ferrous chloride ; $FeCl_3$ is ferric chloride
Hg_2Cl_2 is mercurous chloride ; $HgCl_2$ is mercuric chloride
$SnCl_2$ is stannous chloride ; $SnCl_4$ is stannic chloride
CuCl is cuprous chloride ; $CuCl_2$ is cupric chloride

Modern chemists make use of Roman numerals in place of these trivial names. For example $FeCl_2$ is Iron (II) chloride, $FeCl_3$ is Iron (III) chloride, $SnCl_2$ is Tin (II) chloride and $SnCl_4$ is Tin (IV) chloride.

Different radicals with their symbols and valencies are tabulated in **Table III.**

TABLE III Basic or Electro-positive Radicals

Name	Symbol		Valency
1	2		3
Aluminium	Al		3
Ammonium	NH_4		1
Antimony	Sb		3
Barium	Ba		2
Bismuth	Bi		3
Cadmium	Cd		2
Calcium	Ca		2
Chromium	Cr		3
Cobalt	Co		2
Copper	Cu	*Cuprous or Copper (I)*	1
		Cupric or Copper (II)	2
Hydrogen	H		1
Iron	Fe	*Ferrous or Iron (II)*	2
		Ferric or Iron (III)	3
Lead	Pb	*Plumbous or Lead (II)*	2
		Plumbic or Lead (IV)	4
Magnesium	Mg		2
Manganese	Mn	*Manganous or Manganese (II)*	2
		Manganic or Manganese (III)	
Mercurous	Hg_2	*Mercury (I)*	2
Mercuric	Hg	*Mercury (II)*	2
Nickel	Ni		2
Potassium	K		1
Silver	Ag		1
Sodium	Na		1
Strontium	Sr		2
Tin	Sn	*Stannous or Tin (II)*	2
		Stannic or Tin (IV)	4
Zinc	Zn		2

TABLE IV **Acid or Electro-negative Radicals**

Name	Symbol	Valency
1	2	3
Fluoride	F	1
Chloride	Cl	1
Hypochlorite	ClO	1
Chlorate	ClO_3	1
Bromide	Br	1
Hypobromite	BrO	1
Iodide	I	1
Hypoiodite	IO	1
Iodate	IO_3	1
Sulphide	S	2
Sulphite	SO_3	2
Bisulphite	HSO_3	1
Sulphate	SO_4	2
Bisulphate	HSO_4	1
Thiosulphate	S_2O_3	2
Nitrite	NO_2	1
Nitrate	NO_3	1
Nitride	N	3
Hydroxide	OH	1
Oxide	O	2
Hydride	H	1
Peroxide	O_2	2
Carbonate	CO_3	2
Bicarbonate	HCO_3	1
Carbide	C	4
Phosphate	PO_4	3
Phosphite	HPO_3	2
Phosphide	P	3
Borate	BO_3	3
Acetate	CH_3COO	1

Cyanide	CN	1
Manganate	MnO_4	2
Permanganate	MnO_4	1
Chromate	CrO_4	2
Dichromate	Cr_2O_7	2
Ferrocyanide	$Fe(CN)_6$	4
Ferricyanide	$Fe(CN)_6$	3
Arsenite	AsO_3	3
Arsenate	AsO_4	3
Zincate	ZnO_2	2
Meta-Aluminate	AlO_2	1
Aluminate	AlO_3	3
Stannate	SnO_3	2
Silicate	SiO_3	2

N.B. *The student must learn by heart the symbols and valencies before proceeding further.* For this purpose go through the table once or twice. Now cover the columns 2 and 3 above with a piece of paper and read the names of various radicals from column 1, one by one. Speak out the symbols and valencies of the radicals from your memory and compare by slipping the paper down. If you remember the symbol and valency for a certain radical, well and good, *otherwise repeat it 10 times and attempt the next radical similarly. In this way go through the list again and again till you can repeat both the tables without stumbling even once.*

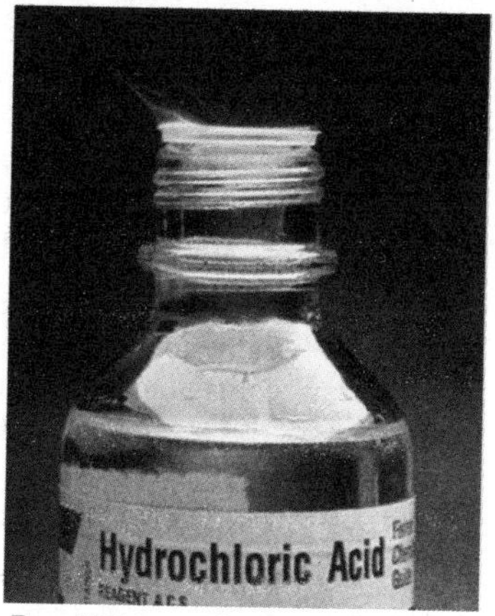

Pure HCl is a colour less gas, hydrochloric acid is an aqueous solution of HCl.

6. Aid to Memory. To remember the symbols and valencies easily and thus be able to write formulae correctly we should know a few correct formulae. If we know these well, writing of formulae will be nothing more than a simple game. Commit the following correct formulae to memory :

1. HCl Hydrogen chloride (Hydochloric acid)
2. $H_2\underline{SO}_4$ Hydrogen sulphate (Sulphuric acid)

3.	$H_2\underline{SO}_3$	Hydrogen sulphite (Sulphurous acid)
4.	$H\underline{NO}_3$	Hydrogen, nitrate (Nitric acid)
5.	$H\underline{NO}_2$	Hydrogen nitrite (Nitrous acid)
6.	HBr	Hydrogen bromide (Hydrobromic acid
7.	HI	Hydrogen iodide (Hydriodic acid)
8.	$H\underline{ClO}_3$	Hydrogen chlorate (Chloric acid)
9.	$H_3\underline{PO}_4$	Hydrogen phosphate (Phosphoric acid)
10.	$H_3\underline{BO}_3$	Hydrogen borate (Boric acid)
11.	$H_2\underline{CO}_3$	Hydrogen carbonate (Carbonic acid)
12.	H_2O	Hydrogen oxide (Water)
13.	$H\underline{OH}$	Hydrogen hydroxide (Water)
14.	H_2S	Hydrogen sulphide (Hydrosulphuric acid)
15.	NaCl	Sodium chloride
16.	$Mg\underline{SO}_4$	Magnesium sulphate
17.	$Ba\underline{SO}_3$	Barium sulphite
18.	$Ag\underline{NO}_3$	Silver nitrate
19.	$Li_4\underline{NO}_2$	Lithium nitrite
20.	AgBr	Silver bromide
21.	CuI	Copper iodide (Cuprous)
22.	$KClO_3$	Potassium chlorate
23.	$Fe\underline{PO}_4$	Iron phosphate (Ferric)
24.	$Al\underline{BO}_3$	Aluminium borate
25.	$Ca\underline{CO}_3$	Calcium carbonate
26.	CoO	Cobalt oxide
27.	$NH_4\underline{OH}$	Ammonium hydroxide
28.	CuS	Copper sulphide (Cupric)

Compounds 1—14 are hydrogen compounds; thus valencies of radicals combined with hydrogen are directly given by the number of hydrogen atoms combined in each case. All compound radicals have been underlined to facilitate their selection.

In compounds 15—28, hydrogen atoms of compounds 1—14 have been replaced by other basic radicals. The positive valency of the basic radicals is equal to the negative valency of the acid radicals with which these are combined. For example:

(*i*) Valency of NO_3 from (4) = 1 and positive valency of Ag from (18) is the same as that of NO_3 *i.e.*, = 1.

(*ii*) Valency of SO_4 from (2) = 2 and positive valency of Mg from (16) is the same as that of SO_4 ; *i.e.*, = 2.

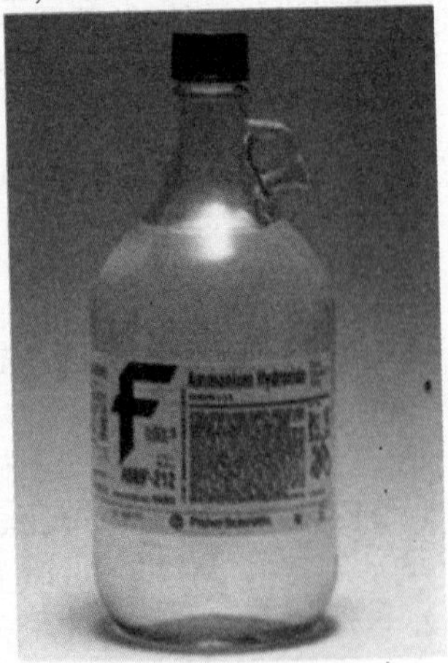

This bottle contains ammonium hydroxide.

(*iii*) Valency of PO_4 from (9) = 3 and positive valency of iron (*ferric*) from (23) is the same as that of PO_4, *i.e.*, = 3, and so on.

7. How to Write a Formula ? In the formation of a chemical compound, combination takes place between the positive and the negative radicals in such a way that the *product of valency and the number of radicals is the same for both the radicals.* Thus to write the formula of a compound we proceed as follows :

(*i*) Write the symbols of the two radicals side by side with valencies at the top, the positive radical to the left and negative radical to the right.

(*ii*) Cross the valencies after removing the common factor, if any. The numbers are to be placed to the lower right of each symbol. The compound radical must be enclosed within a bracket and the number placed outside the bracket to the lower right.

Let us illustrate the process by taking a few examples :

$$BaCO_3$$

Example 1. For writing the formula of sodium sulphate, proceeding as above we have :

(*i*) Writing symbols side by side with valencies at the top.

$$Na^{1+}SO_4^{\ 2-}$$

(*ii*) There being nothing common in 1 and 2, crossing the valencies we get the desired formula:

$$Na_2SO_4$$

Example 2. Similarly for writing the formula of barium carbonate, we have the two steps :

(*i*) Writing the symbols side by side :

$$Ba^{2+}CO_3^{\ 2-}$$

(*ii*) Removing the common factor 2, and crossing the valencies we get the desired formula :

$$BaCO_3$$

Example 3. Formula for aluminium sulphate can be written in the same manner.

(*i*) Writing the symbols side by side :

$$Al^{3+}SO_4^{\ 2-}$$

(*ii*) There being nothing common in valencies 2 and 3 we cross them after enclosing the compound radical SO_4 within brackets, and we have the desired formula :

$$Al_2(SO_4)_3$$

Example 4. To write the formula of iron (III) carbonate.

(*i*) Writing the symbols side by side, we have

$$Fe^{3+}CO_3^{2-}$$

(*ii*) There being nothing common, cross the valencies after enclosing the compound radical with in brackets and we get the desired formula.

$$Fe_2(CO_3)_3$$

Iron ore is scooped in an open-pit mine.

Example 5. To write the formula of ammonium dichromate and proceeding as usual :

1st step	:	$NH_4^{1+}Cr_2O_7^{2-}$
2nd step	:	$(NH_4)_2Cr_2O_7$

Example 6. To write the formula of chromium phosphate we have two steps :

1st step	:	$Cr^{3+}PO_4^{3-}$
2nd step	:	$CrPO_4$

Example 7. To write the formula of iron (II) chloride we have two steps:

1st step	:	$Fe^{2+}Cl^{1-}$
2nd step	:	$FeCl_2$

TEST YOUR UNDERSTANDING

Fill in the blanks in the following :

(*i*) The abbreviation used for the lengthy name of an element is termed ....

(*ii*) .... is not merely an abbreviation for the name of an element, but has a .... significance as well.

(*iii*) C stands for one atom of ....and also for .... by weight of it, this weight being the .... of the element.

(*iv*) the symbolic expression for a molecule is called a .... It has both a .... as well as a .... significance.

(*v*) Co stands for .... and CO stands for ....

(*vi*) Combining capacity of an atom or a radical is called its .... It is equal to the number of .... or .... atoms or double the number of .... atoms which combine with it.

(*vii*) Valency of carbon in CH_4, C_2H_6, C_2H_4 and C_2H_2 is ...., ..., ... and .... respectively.

(*viii*) Valency of iron in $FeCl_2$ and $FeCl_3$ is .... and .... respectively.

(*ix*) Valency of tin in $SnCl_2$ and $SnCl_4$ is .... and .... respectively.

(*x*) Valency of sulphur in SO_2 and SO_3 is .... and .... respectively.

KEY

(*i*) symbol

(*ii*) symbol, quantitative

(*iii*) carbon, 12 amu, atomic weight

(*iv*) formula, qualitative, quantitative

(*v*) the atom of the element cobalt; the molecule of the compound carbon monoxide;

(*vi*) valency, hydrogen, chlorine, oxygen

(*vii*) 4, 3, 2, 1

(*viii*) 2, 3

(*ix*) 2, 4

(*x*) 4, 6.

EXERCISES

I. Proceeding in the manner indicated above write down the formulae of the following compounds :

(1) Aluminium chloride.
(2) Ammonium nitrite.
(3) Barium sulphate.
(4) Bismuth nitrate.
(5) Cadmium carbonate.
(6) Calcium bromide.
(7) Chromium sulphate.
(8) Cobalt nitrate.
(9) Cupric hydroxide.
(10) Cuprous chloride.
(11) Hydrogen peroxide.
(12) Ferrous sulphide.
(13) Lead acetate.
(14) Magnesium phosphate.
(15) Manganous sulphate.
(16) Mercuric iodide.
(17) Nickel nitrate.
(18) Potassium ferrocyanide.
(19) Silver thiosulphate.
(20) Sodium sulphite.
(21) Strontium bromide.
(22) Stannous chloride.

(23) Stannic oxide.
(24) Zinc ferricyanide.
(25) Calcium borate
(26) Potassium permanganate.
(27) Sodium dichromate.
(28) Sodium zincate.
(29) Calcium silicate.
(30) Potassium cyanide.

II. Write down chemical names of substances whose formulae are given below:

(1) $Ca_3(PO_4)_2$
(2) $Ba(ClO_3)_2$
(3) AgCl
(4) NaBrO
(5) K_2CO_3
(6) $Al_2(SO_4)_3$
(7) $Na_2S_2O_3$
(8) Na_2SiO_3
(9) Hg_2Cl_2
(10) $(CH_3COO)_2Pb$
(11) $NaNH_4HPO_4$
(12) $CrCl_3$
(13) $SnCl_2$
(14) K_2MnO_4

Many consumer items are made of aluminium.

(15) $Mg(HCO_3)_2$
(16) Ag_2SO_3
(17) $Mn_3(BO_3)_2$
(18) Cu_2O
(19) $Ca(OH)_2$
(20) $PbCrO_4$
(21) $Na_4Fe(CN)_6$
(22) Ag_3AsO_3
(23) $Sb_2(SO_4)_3$
(24) H_3BO_3.

III. Write down the formulae of the compounds given below :

(1) Ferric sulphate.
(2) Magnesium phosphite.
(3) Aluminium carbonate.
(4) Sodium thiosulphate.
(5) Cadmium nitrate.
(6) Chromium oxide.
(7) Sodium silicate.
(8) Strontium bicarbonate.
(9) Potassium zincate.
(10) Calcium borate.
(11) Sulphuric acid.
(12) Mercuric iodide.
(13) Lead chromate.
(14) Barium peroxide.
(15) Manganous chloride.
(16) Stannic phosphate.
(17) Nickel bisulphate.
(18) Bismuth iodide.
(19) Calcium hypochlorite.
(20) Arsenious oxide.

IV. Complete the table given below.

Acid Radicals → / Basic Radicals ↓	Chloride	Nitrate	Sulphate	Carbonate	Hydroxide
Magnesium	$MgCl_2$	$Mg(NO_3)_2$	$MgSO_4$		
Iron (II)	$FeCl_2$				
Sodium	NaCl				
Zinc	$ZnCl_2$				
Silver					
Copper (II)					
Tin (IV)					
Ammonium					

V. Prepare a table similar to the one given above in Q. IV with acid radicals—Bicarbonate, sulphite, nitrate, phosphate and cyanide and basic radicals—Barium, calcium, cadmium, iron (III), potassium, copper (I), mercurous, strontium, cobalt and mercury (II).

ANSWERS

I.

(1) $AlCl_3$	(2) NH_4NO_2	(3) $BaSO_4$
(4) $Bi(NO_3)_3$	(5) $CdCO_3$	(6) $CaBr_2$
(7) $Cr_2(SO_4)_3$	(8) $Co(NO_3)_2$	(9) $Cu(OH)_2$
(10) CuCl	(11) H_2O_2	(12) FeS
(13) $Pb(CH\ COO)_2$	(14) $Mg_3(PO_4)_2$	(15) $MnSO_4$
(16) HgI_2	(17) $Ni(NO_3)_2$	(18) $K_4Fe(CN)_6$
(19) $Ag_2S_2O_3$	(20) Na_2SO_3	(21) $SrBr_2$
(22) $SnCl_2$	(23) SnO_2	(24) $Zn_3[Fe(CN_6)]$
(25) $Ca_3(BO_3)_2$	(26) $KMnO_4$	(27) $Na_2Cr_2O_7$
(28) Na_2ZnO_2	(29) $CaSiO_3$	(30) KCN

II. (1) Calcium phosphate (2) Barium chlorate
(3) Silver chloride (4) Sodium hypobromite
(5) Potassium carbonate (6) Aluminium sulphate
(7) Sodium thiosulphate (8) Sodium silicate
(9) Mercurous chloride (10) Lead acetate
(11) Sodium ammonium hydrogen phosphate
(12) Chromium chloride (13) Stannous chloride
(14) Potassium manganate (15) Magnesium bicarbonate
(16) Silver sulphite (17) Manganous borate
(18) Cuprous oxide (19) Calcium hydroxide
(20) Lead chromate (21) Sodium ferrocyanide
(22) Silver arsenite (23) Antimony sulphate

III. (1) $Fe_2(SO_4)_3$ (2) $MgHPO_3$ (3) $Al_2(CO_3)_3$
(4) $Na_2S_2O_3$ (5) $Cd(NO_3)_2$ (6) Cr_2O_3
(7) Na_2SiO_3 (8) $Sr(HCO_3)_2$ (9) K_2ZnO_2
(10) $Ca_3(BO_3)_2$ (11) H_2SO_4 (12) HgI_2
(13) $PbCrO_4$ (14) BaO_2 (15) $MnCl_2$
(16) $Sn_3(PO_4)_4$ (17) $Ni(HSO_4)_2$ (18) BiI_3
(19) $Ca(ClO)_2$ (20) As_2O_3.

IV.

Acid Radicals → / Basic Radicals ↓	Chloride	Nitrate	Sulphate	Carbonate	Hydroxide
Magnesium	$MgCl_2$	$Mg(NO_3)_2$	$MgSO_4$	$MgCO_3$	$Mg(OH)_2$
Iron (II)	$FeCl_2$	$Fe(NO_3)_2$	$FeSO_4$	$FeCO_3$	$Fe(OH)_2$
Sodium	$NaCl$	$NaNO_3$	Na_2SO_4	Na_2CO_3	$NaOH$
Zinc	$ZnCl_2$	$Zn(NO_3)_2$	$ZnSO_4$	$ZnCO_3$	$Zn(OH)_2$
Silver	$AgCl$	$AgNO_3$	Ag_2SO_4	Ag_2CO_3	$AgOH$
Copper (II)	$CuCl_2$	$Cu(NO_3)_2$	$CuSO_4$	$CuCO_3$	$Cu(OH)_2$
Tin (IV)	$SnCl_4$	$Sn(NO_3)_4$	$Sn(SO_4)_2$	$Sn(CO_3)_2$	$Sn(OH)_4$
Ammonium	NH_4Cl	NH_4NO_3	$(NH_4)_2SO_4$	$(NH_4)_2CO_3$	NH_4OH

V.

Acid Radicals → / Basic Radicals ↓	Bicarbonate	Sulphite	Nitrite	Phosphate	Cyanide
Barium	$Ba(HCO_3)_2$	$BaSO_3$	$Ba(NO_2)_2$	$Ba_3(PO_4)_2$	$Ba(CN)_2$
Calcium	$Ca(HCO_3)_2$	$CaSO_3$	$Ca(NO_2)_2$	$Ca_3(PO_4)_2$	$Ca(CN)_2$
Cadmium	$Cd(HCO_3)_2$	$CdSO_3$	$Cd(NO_2)_2$	$Cd_3(PO_4)_2$	$Cd(CN)_2$
Iron (III)	$Fe(HCO_3)_3$	$Fe_2(SO_3)_3$	$Fe(NO_2)_3$	$FePO_4$	$Fe(CN)_3$
Potassium	$KHCO_3$	K_2SO_3	KNO_2	K_3PO_4	KCN
Copper (I)	$CuHCO_3$	Cu_2SO_3	$CuNO_2$	Cu_3PO_4	CuCN
Mercurous	$Hg_2(HCO_3)_2$	Hg_2SO_3	$Hg_2(NO_2)_2$	$Hg_6(PO_4)_2$	$Hg_2(CN)_2$
Strontium	$Sr(HCO_3)_2$	$SrSO_3$	$Sr(NO_2)_2$	$Sr_3(PO_4)_2$	$Sr(CN)_2$
Cobalt	$Co(HCO_3)_2$	$CoSO_3$	$Co(NO_2)_2$	$Co_3(PO_4)_2$	$Co(CN)_2$
Mercury (II)	$Hg(HCO_3)_2$	$HgSO_3$	$Hg(NO_2)_2$	$Hg_3(PO_4)_2$	$Hg(CN)_2$

3 CHAPTER

Chemical Equations (I)

1. Chemical Equations. Just as a symbol represents an atom of an element and a formula represents a molecule of a substance, a chemical equation is a symbolic representation of an actual chemical change.

When hydrochloric acid acts on calcium carbonate, calcium chloride and water are formed and carbon dioxide is given out. To represent this chemical change we write

$$CaCO_3 + HCl = CaCl_2 + H_2O + CO_2 \uparrow \qquad ...(i)$$

Michelangelo's glorius statue of David is just a form of calcuim carbonate ($CaCO_3$), a simple ionic compound.

i.e., we (i) write the formulae of the reacting substances towards the left of the sign = ;

(ii) put down the formulae of the various products to the right of the sign = and

(iii) put an arrow-head pointing upwards near CO_2 to show that this substance escapes out.

Such a chemical equation is called a **Skeleton Equation** ; in it the number of atoms of some elements on the two sides is not the same. But if we write

$$CaCO_3 + 2HCl = CaCl_2 + H_2O + CO_2 \uparrow \quad ...(ii)$$

the number of atoms of the different elements on the two sides becomes equal. Such an equation is a **Balanced Chemical Equation**, and this is in accordance with the Law of Conservation of Mass.

Again, let us consider the action of heat on potassium chlorate. It decomposes with the formation of potassium chloride and oxygen and so we write

$$KClO_3 = KCl + 3O$$

This skeleton equation is balanced but here oxygen is represented in the form of atoms, and not molecules. Such an equation is called **Atomic Equation**. This equation must be modified to

$$2KClO_3 = 2KCl + 3O_2 \uparrow$$

in order to remove this defect. Such an equation is called **Molecular Equation**.

2. Essentials of a Chemical Equation. A true chemical equation, therefore, must be in accordance with the following essentials :

(1) It should represent an **actual chemical change**.

(2) It should be **balanced**, *i.e.*, number of atoms of different elements on the two sides of the equation must be equal.

(3) It should be Molecular *i.e.*, all the substances concerned could be expressed as molecules.

3. Limitations of a Chemical Equation. It gives us no information about the following:

(*i*) The physical state of the reactants.

(*ii*) The concentration of the reactants.

(*iii*) The time taken for the reaction to complete.

(*iv*) The rate at which the reaction proceeds.

(*v*) The conditions necessary to start and carry on the reaction *e.g.*, Is any catalyst required? What is the temperature needed to start and continue the reaction?

(*vi*) Is the reaction exothermic or endothermic, *i.e.*, is heat evolved or absorbed during the reaction?

4. Implications of a Chemical Equation. The equation

$$Mg + H_2SO_4 = MgSO_4 + H_2$$

tell us.

(*i*) That under certain conditions not clearly stated, magesium reacts with sulphuric acid to form magnesium sulphate and hydrogen.

(*ii*) That 1 molecule of magnesium containing 1 atom of it, reacts with 1 molecule of sulphuric acid (containing 2 atoms of hydrogen, 1 atom of sulphur and 4 atoms of oxygen) to form 1 molecule of magnesium sulphate (containing 1 atom of magnesium, 1 atom of sulphur and 4 atoms of oxygen) and 1 molecule of hydrogen (containing 2 atoms of it).

(*iii*) That 24 g of magnesium react with 98 g of sulphuric acid producing $(24 + 32 + 64) = 120$ g of magnesium sulphate and 2 g of hydrogen.

(*iv*) That 24 g of magnesium gives 22.4 litres of hydrogen at NTP (*i.e.*, 1 gram molecular volume) by the action of sulphuric acid.

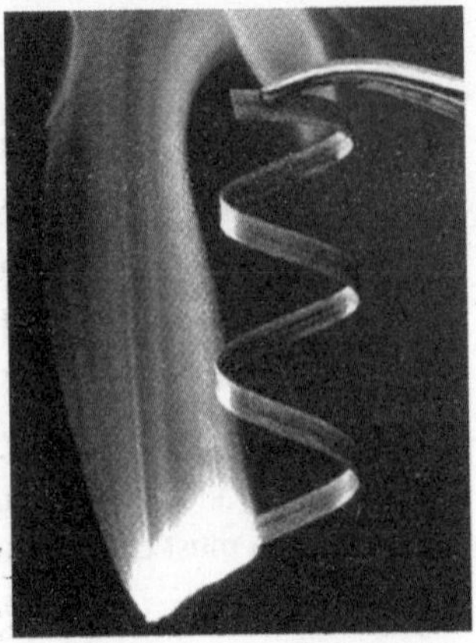

Magnesium (Mg), one of the alkaline earth metals, burns in air.

Thus the above equation has both a qualitative and a quantitative significance, the latter being of very great value in quantitative analysis.

5. How to Balance a Chemical Equation? It should be clearly understood at the very outset that it is undesirable to memorise balanced chemical equations. *An attempt should be made to increase the chemical vocabulary by learning the products of a few different chemical reactions every day* and then balancing of the equations may be done after writing the skeleton equations, by two different methods:

(*i*) Hit and trial method.

(*ii*) Partial equations method.

6. Hit and Trial Method. This method is useful for balancing simple chemical equations and consists in counting up the number of atoms of each element on both sides and trying to equalize them. The following should be borne in mind while trying to balance a chemical equation :

(*i*) The atom which occurs at minimum number of places on both sides should be selected first and one occurring maximum number of times should be taken last of all. For

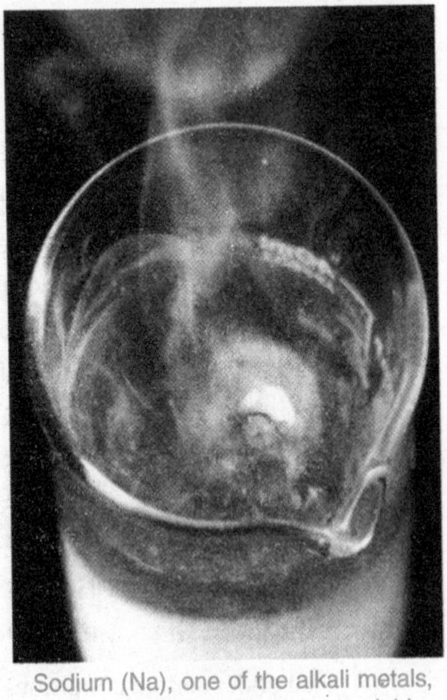

Sodium (Na), one of the alkali metals, reacts violently with water to yield hydrogen gas and an alkaline (basic) solution.

example, while balancing the equation

$$Na + H_2O \rightarrow NaOH + H_2$$

the order of selection should be Na, O and H.

(*a*) There is one sodium atom on both sides; hence it does not require any further equalizing

(*b*) Same is the case with oxygen.

(*c*) There are even number of hydrogen atoms on the L.H.S. (left hand side) being 2, and odd number of these on the R.H.S. (right hand side) being 3. In an attempt to make them even on the R.H.S. also, multiply NaOH by 2. This makes the total number of hydrogen atoms on R.H.S. equal to 4. Multiply H_2O on L.H.S. by 2 to equalize hydrogen atoms and Na by 2 to equalize sodium atoms. Thus balanced equation then would be

$$2Na + 2H_2O \rightarrow 2NaOH + H_2$$

(*ii*) In those cases where an elementary gas like H_2, O_2 or N_2 occurs as a product or is a reactant, it is very helpful to keep it in the atomic state until atoms have been equalized. This gives us **an Atomic equation.** This whole equation is then multiplied by 2 to get the **Molecular equation.** For example, the above equation is very easily balanced if we proceed as indicated below:

$$Na + H_2O \rightarrow NaOH + H$$

The skeleton equation is already balanced and is, therefore, the atomic equation. Multiplying this by 2 to convert it into a molecular equation, the balanced equation then would be:

$$2Na + 2H_2O \rightarrow 2NaOH + H_2$$

Sodium reacts vigorously with water.

Similarly to write the chemical equation for burning of acetylene in oxygen to yield carbon dioxide and water, we write

$$C_2H_2 + O \rightarrow CO_2 + H_2O \quad \textit{(Skeleton Equation)}$$

To equalize carbon, multiply CO_2 by 2. This makes the equation as

$$C_2H_2 + O \rightarrow 2CO_2 + H_2O$$

This makes the total number of oxygen atoms to the right as 5. Therefore, multiply O by 5 to equalize the oxygen atoms. This gives the balanced equation as

$$C_2H_2 + 5O \rightarrow 2CO_2 + H_2O \quad \textit{(Atomic equation)}$$

Now make it molecular by multiplying by 2.

$$2C_2H_2 + 5O_2 \rightarrow 4CO_2 + 2H_2O$$

To illustrate it further, a few more examples are given below :

Example 1. To write the equation for preparation of oxygen by heating potassium chlorate we proceed as follows:

(*i*) $KClO_3 \rightarrow KCl + O$ *(Skeleton Equation)*

(*ii*) To equalize the number of oxygen atoms on both sides multiply O by 3.

$KClO_3 \rightarrow KCl + 3O$ *(Atomic Equation)*

(*iii*) Now multiply it by 2 to make it molecular.

$2KClO_3 \rightarrow 2KCl + 3O_2$ *(Molecular Equation)*

Example 2. Proceeding similarly for the preparation of ammonia by heating a mixture of ammonium chloride and calcium hydroxide, we get

(*i*) $NH_4Cl + Ca(OH)_2 \rightarrow CaCl_2 + NH_3 + H_2O$ *(Skeleton Equation)*

(*ii*) To equalize Cl-atoms multiply NH_2Cl by 2.

$2NH_4Cl + Ca(OH)_2 \rightarrow CaCl_2 + NH_3 + H_2O$

(*iii*) Now to equalize nitrogen atoms multiply NH_3 by 2.

$2NH_4Cl + Ca(OH)_2 \rightarrow CaCl_2 + 2NH_3 + H_2O$

(*iv*) To equalize oxygen atoms multiply H_2O by 2. This will also equalize hydrogen atoms, giving us the balanced equation as

$2NH_4Cl + Ca(OH)_2 \rightarrow CaCl_2 + 2NH_3 + 2H_2O$

Example 3. Sulphur dioxide is prepared by heating copper chips with conc. H_2SO_4. Writing of chemical equation for the reaction involves the following steps:

(*i*) $Cu + H_2SO_4 \rightarrow CuSO_4 + SO_2 + H_2O$ *(Skeleton Equation)*

(*ii*) To equalize sulphur atoms multiply H_2SO_4 by 2.

$Cu + 2H_2SO_4 \rightarrow CuSO_4 + SO_2 + H_2O$

(*iii*) Now to equalize hydrogen atoms, multiply H_2O by 2.
This gives us the balanced equation

$Cu + 2H_2SO_4 \rightarrow CuSO_4 + SO_2 + 2H_2O$

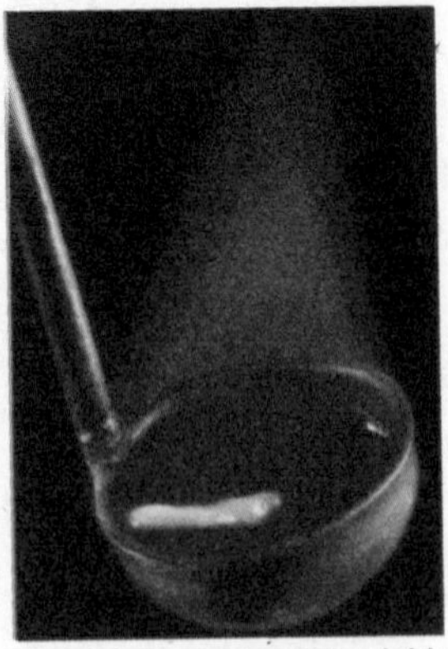

Sulphur burns in air to yield SO_2.

Example 4. Hydrochloric acid decomposes sodium thiosulphate to give sodium chloride, sulphur dioxide and a precipitate of sulphur. Translating this reaction into language of chemistry we have

(*i*) Writing the skeleton equation

$$Na_2S_2O_3 + HCl \rightarrow NaCl + SO_2 + S + H_2O$$

(*ii*) To equalize Na-atoms, multiply NaCl by 2.

$$Na_2S_2O_3 + HCl \rightarrow 2NaCl + SO_2 + S + H_2O$$

(*iii*) To equalize chlorine atoms multiply HCl by 2. This gives us the balanced equation

$$Na_2S_2O_3 + 2HCl \rightarrow 2NaCl + SO_2 + S + H_2O$$

Example 5. Balancing of the skeleton equation for the reduction of As_2O_3 by acidified $SnCl_2$ is done as follows:

(*i*) Writing the skeleton equation

$$As_2O_3 + SnCl_2 + HCl \rightarrow SnCl_2 + As + H_2O$$

(*ii*) To equalize arsenic and oxygen atoms multiply As by 2 and H_2O by 3.

$$As_2O_3 + SnCl_2 + HCl \rightarrow SnCl_4 + 2As + 3H_2O$$

(*iii*) To equalize hydrogen atoms multiply HCl by 6.

$$As_2O_3 + SnCl_2 + 6HCl \rightarrow SnCl_4 + 2As + 3H_2O$$

(*iv*) There are 8 chlorine atoms on the L.H.S. and 4 on the R.H.S. If we multiply $SnCl_4$ by 2 the number of Sn atoms will become different. Then if we multiply $SnCl_2$ by 2 to equalize Sn atoms, the number of chlorine atoms will become different. Hence we should try some other number.

(*v*) Multiply $SnCl_2$ and $SnCl_4$ both by 3. This will equalize chlorine atoms and at the same time will keep the number of Sn atoms equal. This gives us the balanced equation.

$$As_2O_3 + 3SnCl_2 + 6HCl \rightarrow 3SnCl_4 + 2As + 3H_2O$$

7. Thermochemical Equations. Chemical equations for exothermic or endothermic reactions representing the quantity of heat evolved or absorbed during the reaction, are called **thermochemical equations,** *e.g.*,

$$C + O_2 \rightarrow CO_2 + 94{,}300 \text{ cal.}$$

or

$$C + O_2 \rightarrow CO_2 + 94.3 \text{ kcal.}$$

From the equation we learn that when 12 g of carbon combine with 32 g of oxygen on burning to give carbon dioxide, 94,300 calories of 94.3 kcal (kilogram-calories) of heat are evolved.

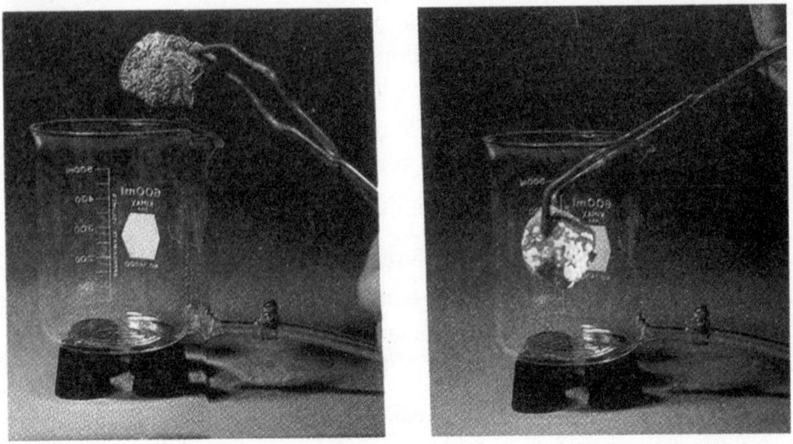

Carbon burns brilliantly in pure O_2 to form CO_2.

8. Physical States of Reactants and Products. It is quite helpful if an equation gives an idea about the physical state of reactants and products of a chemical reaction. This is indicated by writing letters (*g*), (*l*) or (*s*) to represent gas, liquid or solid respectively. Thus the equation for the production of water by the reaction of hydrogen and oxygen (in the presence of an electric spark) at room temperature becomes:

$$2H_2(g) + O_2(g) \longrightarrow 2H_2O\,(l)$$

Burning of aluminium in oxygen to form aluminium oxide can be written as :

$$4Al(s) + 3O_2(g) \longrightarrow 2Al_2O_3(s)$$

When ignited, hydrogen gas reacts completely with oxygen to yield water.

In case a product is precipitated, it is indicated by an arrow pointing downwards (↓)while a gaseous product is indicated by an arrow pointing upwards. A reactant in aqueous solution is indicated by putting (*aq*) after its symbol. For precipitation of silver chloride on mixing aqueous solutions of sodium chloride and silver nitrate and evolution of hydrogen when zinc reacts with hydrochloric acid are represented as follows:

$$NaCl(aq) + AgNO_3(aq) \longrightarrow AgCl \downarrow + NaNO_3$$

$$Zn(s) + 2HCl\,(aq) \longrightarrow ZnCl_2 + H_2 \uparrow$$

TEST YOUR UNDERSTANDING

Fill in the blanks in the following :

(*i*) Shorthand method of writing a chemical reaction with the help of .....is called ....

(*ii*) A chemical equation should be.....and....... It should represent a /an....

(*iii*) $C + O_2 \longrightarrow CO_2 + 94.3$ kcal is an example of a......representing an.....(endothermic /exothermic) reaction.

(*iv*) $KClO_3 \longrightarrow KCl + O$ is an example of a /an....equation.

(*v*) $KClO_3 \longrightarrow KCl + 3O$ is an example of a /an....equation.

(*vi*) $2KClO_3 \longrightarrow 2KCl + 3O_2$ is an example of a /an....equation.

(*vii*) $CaCO_3(s) + 2HCl(aq) \longrightarrow CaCl_2 + CO_2 \uparrow + H_2O$

In the above equation $CaCO_3$ is in ..... HCl is in .... and CO_2 is in .....

(*viii*) A chemical equation gives us no information about the following:

(*a*) ..... and ..... of the reactants.

(*b*) .... for the reaction to complete or .... at which the reaction proceeds.

(*c*) .... to start and carry on the reaction like .... and ....

(*d*) Heat .... or .... in the reaction.

KEY

(*i*) formulae, an equation.

(*ii*) balanced, molecular; actual chemical change.

(*iii*) Thermochemical equation, exothermic.

(*iv*) skeleton:

(*v*) atomic;

(*vi*) molecular;

(*vii*) solid state, aqueous solution, gaseous state.

(*viii*) (*a*) physical state, concentration; (*b*) time taken, rate; (*c*) conditions necessary, temperature, catayst; (*d*) evolved, absorbed.

EXERCISES

I. Translate the following chemical equations written in words into language of chemistry and balance them by hit and trial method.

1. Sodium + Water → Sodium hydroxide + Hydrogen.
2. Calcium + Water → Calcium hydroxide + Hydrogen.

3. Calcium carbonate + Hydrochloric acid → Calcium Chloride + Carbon dioxide + Water.
4. Sodium hydroxide + Sulphuric acid → Sodium sulphate + Water.
5. Sodium carbonate + Nitric acid → Sodium nitrate + Carbon dioxide + Water.
6. Potassium bicarbonate + Sulphuric acid → Potassium sulphate + Carbon dioxide + Water.
7. Sodium peroxide + Water → Sodium hydroxide + Oxygen.
8. Calcium hydroxide + Carbon dioxide → Calcium carbonate + Water.
9. Calcium hydroxide + Carbon dioxide → Calcium bicarbonate.
10. Calcium bicarbonate + Calcium hydroxide → Calcium carbonate + Water.
11. Iron + Sulphuric acid → Ferrous sulphate + Hydrogen.
12. Magnesium + Hydrochloric acid → Magnesium Chloride + Hydrogen.
13. Zinc + Sodium hydroxide → Sodium Zincate + Hydrogen.
14. Aluminium + Sodium hydroxide + Water → Sodium Meta-aluminate + Hydrogen.
15. Tin + Sodium hydroxide + Water → Sodium stannate + Hydrogen.
16. Calcium hydride + Water → Calcium hydroxide + Hydrogen.
17. Silicon + Sodium hydroxide + Water → Sodium silicate + Hydrogen.
18. Mercuric Oxide $\xrightarrow{\text{heat}}$ Mercury + Oxygen.

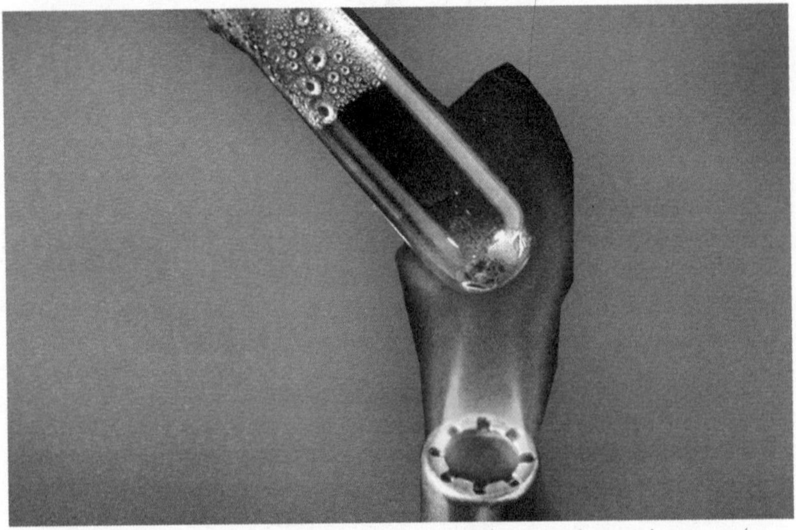

Heating, HgO (a red powder) causes it to decompose into elemental mercury (a silvery liquid) and oxygen (a colourless gas).

19. Zinc oxide + Chlorine → Zinc chloride + Oxygen.
20. Potassium nitrate → Potassium nitrite + Oxygen.
21. Lead (II) nitrate $\xrightarrow{\text{heat}}$ Lead oxide + Nitrogen dioxide + Oxygen.
22. Ammonium nitrate $\xrightarrow{\text{heat}}$ Nitrous oxide + Water.
23. Ammonia + Oxygen → Nitrous oxide + Water.
24. Hydrochloric acid + Oxygen → Chlorine + Water.
25. Silver oxide + Hydrogen per oxide → Silver + Water + Oxygen.
26. Stannous chloride + Mercuric chloride → Stannic chloride + Mercurous chloride.
27. Mercuric chloride + Potassiumiodide → Mercuric iodide + Potassiumchloride.
28. Sulphuric acid + Hydriodicacid → Sulphur dioxide + Iodine + Water.
29. Sulphur dioxide + Hydrogensulphide → Sulphur + Water.
30. Aluminium oxide + Hydrochloric acid → Aluminium chloride + Water
31. Barium peroxide + Hydrochloric acid → Barium chloride + Water + Oxygen.
32. Manganese dioxide + Hydrochloricacid → Manganous chloride + Chlorine + Water.
33. Manganese dioxide + Sulphuric acid → Manganous sulphate + Water + Oxygen.
34. Ammonium sulphate + Sodium hydroxide → Sodium sulphate + Ammonia + Water.
35. Water + Chlorine → Hydrochloric acid + Oxygen.
36. Sulphur dioxide + Water + Iodine → Sulphuric acid + Hydriodic acid.
37. Sodium sulphite + Water + Iodine → Sodium sulphate + Hydriodic acid.
38. Sodium silicate + Hydrofluoric acid → Sodium fluoride + Water + Silicon dioxide or silica.
39. Aluminium chloride + Water → Aluminium hydroxide + Hydrochloric acid.
40. Boron trichloride + Water → Boric acid + Hydro-chloric acid.
41. Potassium bromide + Phosphoric acid → Potassium phosphate + Hydrobromic acid.
42. Bromine + Potassium hydroxide → Potassium bromide + Potassium bromate + Water.
43. Chlorine + Hydriodic acid → Hydrochloric acid + Iodine.
44. Ferric sulphide + Oxygen + Water → Ferric hydroxide + Sulphur.
45. Antimony sulphide + Hydrochloric acid → Antimony chloride + Hydorchloric acid.

46. Sodium sulphate + Carbon → Sodium sulphide + Carbon monoxide.
47. Chlorine+Sulphur dioxide + Water → Sulphuric acid + Hydrochloric acid.
48. Ferric sulphate + Sulphur dioxide + Water → Ferrous sulphate + Sulphuric acid.
49. Potassium permanganate → Potassium manganate + Manganese dioxide + Oxygen.
50. Potassium permanganate + conc. Sulphuric acid → Potassium sulphate + Manganous sulphate + Water + Oxygen.
51. Potassium dichromate + conc. Sulphuric acid → Potassium sulphate + Chromium sulphate + Water + Oxygen.
52. Sulphur + Sulphuric acid → Sulphur dioxide + Water.
53. Ammonia + Chlorine → Ammonium chloride + Nitrogen.

Ammonia is used as a fertilizer to supply nitrogen to growing plants.

54. Calcium phosphate + Silica + Carbon → Calcium silicate + Phosphorus + Carbon monoxide.
55. Phosphorus + Sulphuric acid → Phosphoric acid + Sulphur dioxide + Water.

II. Balance the following skeleton equations by hit and trial method :

1. $C_2H_4 + O_2 \rightarrow CO_2 + H_2O$
2. $C_2H_2 + O_2 \rightarrow CO_2 + H_2O$
3. $CH_4 + O_2 \rightarrow CO_2 + H_2O$
4. $NH_3 + Na \rightarrow NaNH_2 + H_2$
5. $Cr(OH)_3 + Na_2O_2 \rightarrow Na_2CrO_4 + H_2O + NaOH$
6. $Mn(OH)_2 + Na_2O_2 \rightarrow Na_2MnO_4 + NaOH$

7. $Al_2(SO_4)_3 + NaOH \rightarrow Al(OH)_3 + Na_2SO_4$
8. $KI + H_2SO_4 \rightarrow KHSO_4 + H_2O + SO_2 + I_2$
9. $CuFeS_2 + O_2 \rightarrow Cu_2S + FeS + SO_2$
10. $FeS + O_2 \rightarrow FeO + SO_2$
11. $Cu_2S + O_2 \rightarrow Cu_2O + SO_2$
12. $Cu_2S + CuSO_4 \rightarrow Cu + SO_2$
13. $Cu_2O + Cu_2S \rightarrow Cu + SO_2$
14. $CuSO_4 + KI \rightarrow CuI + I_2 + K_2SO_4$
15. $CuCl_2 + H_2O + SO_2 \rightarrow CuCl + HCl + H_2SO_4$
16. $CuCl + SO_2 + HCl \rightarrow CuCl_2 + H_2O + S$
17. $NaAg(CN)_2 + Zn \rightarrow NaCN + Zn(CN)_2 + Ag$
18. $FeCl_3 + NH_4CNS \rightarrow Fe(CNS)_3 + NH_4Cl$
19. $Ca_3(PO_4)_2 + H_2SO_4 \rightarrow Ca(H_2PO_4)_2 + CaSO_4$
20. $CaCN_2 + H_2O \rightarrow CaCO_3 + NH_3$
21. $Mg + HNO_3 \rightarrow Mg(NO_3)_2 + NH_4NO_3 + H_2O$
22. $S + HNO_3 \rightarrow H_2SO_4 + NO_2 + H_2O$
23. $Hg_2(NO_3)_2 \rightarrow Hg + NO_2 + O_2$
24. $AlN + H_2O \rightarrow Al(OH)_3 + NH_3$
25. $Mn_3O_4 + Al \rightarrow Al_2O_3 + Mn$

III. Rewrite the following equations in the language of chemistry and balance by the hit and trial method :

1. Zinc Sulphate $\xrightarrow{\text{heat}}$ Zinc Oxide + Sulphur dioxide + Oxygen.
2. Zinc + Sulphuric acid $\xrightarrow{\text{heat}}$ Zinc sulphate + Sulphur dioxide + Water.
3. Zinc nitrate $\xrightarrow{\text{heat}}$ Zinc oxide + Nitrogen dioxide + Oxygen.
4. Cobalt nitrate $\xrightarrow{\text{heat}}$ Cobalt oxide + Nitrogen dioxide + Oxygen.
5. Lead sulphate + Lead sulphide $\rightarrow$ Lead + Sulphur dioxide.
6. Aluminium + Sulphuric Acid $\rightarrow$ Aluminium sulphate + Sulphur dioxide + Water.

7. Aluminium oxide + Potassium hydroxide → Potassium meta-aluminate + water.
8. Stannic oxide + Potassium hydroxide → Potassium stannate + Water.
9. Ferric chloride + Stannous chloride → Ferrous chloride + Stannic chloride.
10. Lead oxide + Sodium hydroxide → Sodium plumbite + Water.
11. Lead dioxide + Sulphuric acid → Lead sulphate + Water + Oxygen.
12. Lead acetate + Potassium chromate → Leadchromate + Potassium acetate.
13. Arsenic + Sodium hydroxide → Sodium arsenite + Hydrogen.
14. Arsenic + Sulphuric acid → Arsenic acid + Sulphur dioxide + Water.
15. Arsenious oxide + Iodine + Water → Arsenic acid + Hydriodic acid.
16. Arsenious oxide + Hydrochloric acid → Arsenious chloride + Water.
17. Arsenious oxide + Chlorine + Water → Arsenic oxide + Hydrochloric acid.
18. Arsenious acid + Hydrogen sulphide → Arsenious sulphide + Water.
19. Antimony chloride + Water → Antimony trioxide + Hydrochloric acid.
20. Bismuth + Nitric acid → Bismuth nitrate + Nitrogen dioxide + Water.
21. Bismuth trioxide + Hydrochloric acid → Bismuth trichloride + Water.
22. Chromium oxide + Sodium hydroxide + Oxygen → Sodium chromate + Water.
23. Chromium oxide + Sulphuric acid → Chromium sulphate + Water.
24. Potassium dichromate → Potassium chromate + Chromium oxide + Oxygen.
25. Potassium dichromate + Potassium hydroxide → Potassium chromate + Water.
26. Manganese tetrachloride + Water → Manganese dioxide + Hydrochloric acid.
27. Manganese dioxide + Sulphuric acid → Manganic sulphate + Water + Oxygen.
28. Ferrous sulphate + Manganese dioxide + Sulphuric acid → Ferric sulphate + Manganous sulphate + water.
29. Potassium manganate + Chlorine → Potassium permanganate + Potassium chloride
30. Potassium manganate + Carbon dioxide → Potassium carbonate + Potassium permanganate + Manganese dioxide.
31. Manganese dioxide + Potassium hydroxide + Oxygen → Potassium Manganate + Water.

32. Carbon + Ferric oxide → Carbon monoxide + Iron.
33. Silicon + Ferric oxide → Silica + Iron.
34. Ferrous sulphate + Sulphuric acid → Ferric sulphate + Water + Sulphur dioxide.
35. Ferrous sulphate → Ferric oxide + Sulphur dioxide + Sulphur trioxide.
36. Ferric chloride + Water → Ferric hydroxide + Hydrochloric acid.
37. Ferric chloride + Nascent hydrogen → Ferrous chloride + Hydrochloric acid.
38. Lead sulphide + Hydrogen peroxide → Lead sulphate + Water.
39. Copper oxide + Ammonia → Copper + Nitrogen + Water.
40. Potassium nitrate + Ferrous chloride + Hydrochloric acid → Potassium chloride + Ferric chloride + Nitric oxide + Water.
41. Potassium permanganate + Sulphuric acid + Nascent hydrogen → Potassium sulphate + Manganous sulphate + Water.
42. Stannous chloride + Ozone + Hydrochloric acid → Stannic chloride + Water.
43. Calcium phosphide + Water → Calcium hydroxide + Phosphine.
44. Magnesium bicarbonate + Calcium hydroxide → Magnesium carbonate + Calcium carbonate + Water.
45. Sodium carbonate + Hydrogen peroxide → Sodium peroxide + Carbon dioxide + Water.
46. Potassium permanganate + Hydrochloric acid → Potassium chloride + Manganous chloride + Water + Chlorine.
47. Potassium dichromate + Hydrochloric acid → Potassium chloride + Chromium chloride + Water + Chlorine.

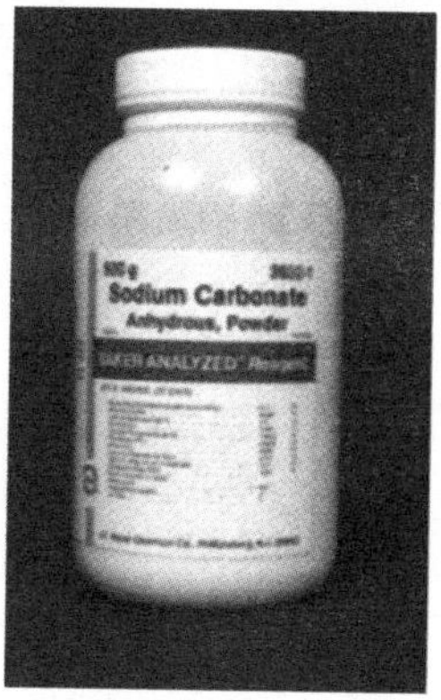

Sodium carbonate is often used is a primary standard for acids.

48. Lead peroxide + Hydrochloric acid → Plumbous chloride + Chlorine + Water.
49. Sodium sulphite + Bromine + Water → Sodium sulphate + Hydrobromic acid.
50. Bromine + Potassium hydroxide (cold) → Potassium bromide + Potassium hypobromite + Water.

IV. How are the following symbolised in a chemical equation :

(*i*) A precipitate being formed,

(*ii*) A reactant being in an aqueous solution,

(*iii*) A gaseous product being evolved, and

(*iv*) A reaction being exothermic.

ANSWERS

I.

1. $2Na$	$+ 2H_2O$	$= 2NaOH$	$+ H_2$
2. Ca	$+ 2H_2O$	$= Ca(OH)_2$	$+ H_2$
3. $CaCO_3$	$+ 2HCl$	$= CaCl_2$	$+ CO_2 + H_2O$
4. $2NaOH$	$+ H_2SO_4$	$= Na_2SO_4$	$+ 2H_2O$
5. Na_2CO_3	$+ 2HNO_3$	$= 2NaNO_3$	$+ CO_2 + H_2O$
6. $2KHCO_3$	$+ H_2SO_4$	$= K_2SO_4$	$+ 2CO_2 + 2H_2O$
7. $2Na_2O_2$	$+ 2H_2O$	$= 4NaOH$	$+ O_2$
8. $Ca(OH)_2$	$+ CO_2$	$= CaCO_3$	$+ H_2O$
9. $Ca(OH)_2$	$+ 2CO_2$	$= Ca(HCO_3)_2$	
10. $Ca(HCO_3)_2$	$+ Ca(OH)_2$	$= 2CaCO_3$	$+ 2H_2O$
11. Fe	$+ H_2SO_4$	$= FeSO_4$	$+ H_2$
12. Mg	$+ 2HCl$	$= MgCl_2$	$+ H_2$
13. Zn	$+ 2NaOH$	$= Na_2ZnO_2$	$+ H_2$
14. $2Al + 2NaOH$	$+ 2H_2O$	$= 2NaAlO_2$	$+ 3H_2$
15. $Sn + 2NaOH$	$+ H_2O$	$= Na_2SnO_3$	$+ 2H_2$
16. CaH_2	$+ 2H_2O$	$= Ca(OH)_2$	$+ 2H_2$
17. $Si + 2NaOH$	$+ H_2O$	$= Na_2SiO_3$	$+ 2H_2$
18. $2HgO$		$= 2Hg$	$+ O_2$
19. $2ZnO$	$+ 2Cl_2$	$= 2ZnCl_2$	$+ O_2$
20. $2KNO_3$		$= 2KNO_2$	$+ O_2$
21. $2Pb(NO_3)_2$		$=2PbO$	$+ 4NO_2 + O_2$
22. NH_4NO_3		$= N_2O$	$+ 2H_2O$
23. $4NH_3$	$+ 5O_2$	$=4NO$	$+ 6H_2O$
24. $4HCl$	$+ O_2$	$= 2Cl_2$	$+ 2H_2O$
25. Ag_2O	$+ H_2O_2$	$= 2Ag$	$+ H_2O + O_2$
26. $SnCl_2$	$+ 2HgCl_2$	$= SnCl_4$	$+ Hg_2Cl_2$
27. $HgCl_2$	$+ 2KI$	$= HgI_2$	$+ 2KCl$
28. H_2SO_4	$+ 2HI$	$= SO_2$	$+ I_2 + 2H_2O$
29. SO_2	$+ 2H_2S$	$= 3S$	$+ 2H_2O$
30. Al_2O_3	$+ 6HCl$	$= 2AlCl_3$	$+ 3H_2O$
31. $2BaO_2$	$+ 4HCl$	$= 2BaCl_2$	$+ 2H_2O + O_2$
32. MnO_2	$+ 4HCl$	$= MnCl_2$	$+ Cl_2 + 2H_2O$
33. $2MnO_2$	$+ 2H_2SO_4$	$= 2MnSO_4$	$+ 2H_2O + O_2$
34. $(NH_4)_2SO_4$	$+ 2NaOH$	$= Na_2SO_4$	$+ 2NH_3 + 2H_2O$

35. $2H_2O + 2Cl_2 = 4HCl + O_2$

36. $SO_2 + 2H_2O + I_2 = H_2SO_4 + 2HI$

37. $Na_2SO_3 + H_2O + I_2 = Na_2SO_4 + 2HI$

38. $Na_2SiO_3 + 2HF = 2NaF + H_2O + SiO_2$

39. $AlCl_3 + 3H_2O = Al(OH)_3 + 3HCl$

40. $BCl_3 + 3H_2O = H_3BO_3 + 3HCl$

41. $3KBr + H_3PO_4 = K_3PO_4 + 3HBr$

42. $3Br_2 + 6KOH = 5KBr + KBrO_3 + 3H_2O$

43. $Cl_2 + 2HI = 2HCl + I_2$

44. $2Fe_2S_3 + 3O_2 + 6H_2O = 4Fe(OH)_3 + 6S$

45. $Sb_2S_3 + 6HCl = 2SbCl_3 + 3H_2S$

46. $Na_2SO_4 + 4C = Na_2S + 4CO$

47. $Cl_2 + SO_2 + 2H_2O = H_2SO_4 + 2HCl$

48. $Fe_2(SO_4)_3 + SO_2 + 2H_2O = 2FeSO_4 + 2H_2SO_4$

49. $2KMnO_4 = K_2MnO_4 + MnO_2 + O_2$

50. $4KMnO_4 + 6H_2SO_4 = 2K_2SO_4 + 4MnSO_4 + 6H_2O + 5O_2$

51. $2K_2Cr_2O_7 + 8H_2SO_4 = 2K_2SO_4 + 2Cr_2(SO_4)_3 + 6H_2O + 3O_2$

52. $S + 2H_2SO_4 = 3SO_2 + 2H_2O$

53. $8NH_3 + 3Cl_2 = 6NH_4Cl + N_2$

54. $Ca_3(PO_4)_2 + 3SiO_2 + 5C = 3CaSiO_3 + 2P + 5CO$

55. $2P + 5H_2SO_4 = 2H_3PO_4 + 5SO_2 + 2H_2O$

II.

1. $C_2H_4 + 3O_2 = 2CO_2 + 2H_2O$
2. $2C_2H_2 + 5O_2 = 4CO_2 + 2H_2O$
3. $CH_4 + 2O_2 = CO_2 + 2H_2O$
4. $2NH_3 + 2Na = 2NaNH_2 + H_2$
5. $2Cr(OH)_3 + 3Na_2O_2 = 2Na_2CrO_4 + 2H_2O + 2\ NaOH$
6. $Mn(OH)_2 + 2Na_2O_2 = Na_2MnO_4 + 2NaOH$
7. $Al_2(SO_4)_3 + 6NaOH = 2Al(OH)_3 + 3Na_2SO_4$
8. $2KI + 3H_2SO_4 = 2KHSO_4 + 2H_2O + SO_2 + I_2$
9. $2CuFeS_2 + O_2 = Cu_2S + 2FeS + SO_2$
10. $2FeS + 3O_2 = 2FeO + 2SO_2$
11. $2Cu_2S + 3O_2 = 2Cu_2O + 2SO_2$
12. $Cu_2S + CuSO_4 = 3\ Cu + 2SO_2$
13. $2Cu_2O + Cu_2S = 6Cu + SO_2$
14. $2CuSO_4 + 3KI = 2CuI + I_2 + 2K_2SO_4$

15. $2CuCl_2 + 2H_2O + SO_2 = 2CuCl + 2HCl + H_2SO_4$
16. $4CuCl + SO_2 + 4HCl = 4CuCl_2 + 2H_2O + S$
17. $2NaAg(CN)_2 + Zn = 2NaCN + Zn(CN)_2 + 2Ag$
18. $FeCl_3 + 3NH_4CNS = Fe(CNS)_3 + 3NH_4Cl$
19. $Ca_3(PO_4)_2 + 2H_2SO_4 = Ca(H_2PO_4)_2 + 2CaSO_4$
20. $CaCN_2 + 3H_2O = CaCO_3 + 2NH_3$
21. $4Mg + 10HNO_3 = 4Mg(NO_3)_2 + NH_4NO_3 + 3H_2O$
22. $S + 6HNO_3 = H_2SO_4 + 6NO_2 + 2H_2O$
23. $Hg_2(NO_3)_2 = 2Hg + 2NO_2 + O_2$
24. $AlN + 3H_2O = Al(OH)_3 + NH_3$
25. $3Mn_3O_4 + 8\,Al = 4Al_2O_3 + 9\,Mn$

III.

1. $2ZnSO_4 = 2ZnO + 2SO_2 + O_2$
2. $Zn + 2H_2SO_4 = ZnSO_4 + SO_2 + 2H_2O$
3. $2Zn(NO_3)_2 = 2ZnO + 4NO_2 + O_2$
4. $2Co(NO_3)_2 = 2CoO + 4NO_2 + O_2$
5. $PbS + PbSO_4 = 2Pb + 2SO_2$
6. $2Al + 6H_2SO_4 = Al_2(SO_4)_3 + 3SO_2 + 6H_2O$
7. $Al_2O_3 + 2KOH = 2KAlO_2 + H_2O$
8. $SnO_2 + 2KOH = K_2SnO_3 + H_2O$
9. $2FeCl_3 + SnCl_2 = 2FeCl_2 + SnCl_4$
10. $PbO + 2NaOH = Na_2PbO_2 + H_2O$
11. $2PbO_2 + 2H_2SO_4 = 2PbSO_4 + 2H_2O + O_2$
12. $(CH_3COO)_2Pb + K_2CrO_4 = PbCrO_4 + 2CH_3COOK$
13. $2As + 6NaOH = 2Na_3AsO_3 + 3H_2$
14. $2As + 5H_2SO_4 = 2H_3AsO_4 + 5SO_2 + 2H_2O$
15. $As_2O_3 + 2I_2 + 5H_2O = 2H_3AsO_4 + 4HI$
16. $As_2O_3 + 6HCl = 2AsCl_3 + 3H_2O$
17. $As_2O_3 + 2Cl_2 + 2H_2O = As_2O_5 + 4HCl$
18. $2H_3AsO_3 + 3H_2S = As_2S_3 + 6H_2O$
19. $2SbCl_3 + 3H_2O = Sb_2O_3 + 6HCl$
20. $Bi + 6HNO_3 = Bi(NO_3)_3 + 3NO_2 + 3H_2O$
21. $Bi_2O_3 + 6HCl = 2BiCl_3 + 3H_2O$
22. $2Cr_2O_3 + 8NaOH + 3O_2 = 4Na_2CrO_4 + 4H_2O$
23. $Cr_2O_3 + 3H_2SO_4 = Cr_2(SO_4)_3 + 3H_2O$
24. $4K_2Cr_2O_7 = 4K_2CrO_4 + 2Cr_2O_3 + 3O_2$
25. $K_2Cr_2O_7 + 2KOH = 2K_2CrO_4 + H_2O$
26. $MnCl_4 + 2H_2O = MnO_2 + 4HCl$

27. $4MnO_2 + 6H_2SO_4 = 2Mn_2(SO_4)_3 + 6H_2O + O_2$
28. $2FeSO_4 + MnO_2 + 2H_2SO_4 = Fe_2(SO_4)_3 + MnSO_4 + 2H_2O$
29. $2K_2MnO_4 + Cl_2 = 2KMnO_4 + 2KCl$
30. $3K_2MnO_4 + 2CO_2 = 2K_2CO_3 + 2KMnO_4 + MnO_2$
31. $2MnO_2 + 4KOH + O_2 = 2K_2MnO_4 + 2H_2O$
32. $3C + Fe_2O_3 = 3CO + 2Fe$
33. $3Si + 2Fe_2O_3 = 3SiO_2 + 4Fe$
34. $2FeSO_4 + 2H_2SO_4 = Fe_2(SO_4)_3 + 2H_2O + SO_2$
35. $2FeSO_4 = Fe_2O_3 + SO_2 + SO_3$
36. $FeCl_3 + 3H_2O = Fe(OH)_3 + 3HCl$
37. $FeCl_3 + H = FeCl_2 + HCl$
38. $PbS + 4H_2O_2 = PbSO_4 + 4H_2O$
39. $3CuO + 2NH_3 = 3Cu + N_2 + 3H_2O$

The copper dome on this building is green because the copper has reacted with oxygen in the air to form copper oxide which then reacted very slowly with water to form green copper hydroxide.

40. $KNO_3 + 3FeCl_2 + 4HCl = KCl + 3FeCl_3 + NO + 2H_2O$
41. $2KMnO_4 + 3H_2SO_4 + 10H = K_2SO_4 + 2MnSO_4 + 8H_2O$
42. $3SnCl_2 + O_3 + 6HCl = 3SnCl_4 + 3H_2O$
43. $Ca_3P_2 + 6H_2O = 3Ca(OH)_2 + 2PH_3$
44. $Mg(HCO_3)_2 + Ca(OH)_2 = MgCO_3 + CaCO_3 + 2H_2O$
45. $Na_2CO_3 + H_2O_2 = Na_2O_2 + CO_2 + H_2O$
46. $2KMnO_4 + 16HCl = 2KCl + 2MnCl_2 + 8H_2O + 5Cl_2$
47. $K_2Cr_2O_7 + 14HCl = 2KCl + 2CrCl_3 + 7H_2O + 3Cl_2$
48. $PbO_2 + 4HCl = PbCl_2 + Cl_2 + 2H_2O$
49. $Na_2SO_3 + Br_2 + H_2O = Na_2SO_4 + 2HBr$
50. $Br_2 + 2KOH = KBr + KBrO + H_2O$

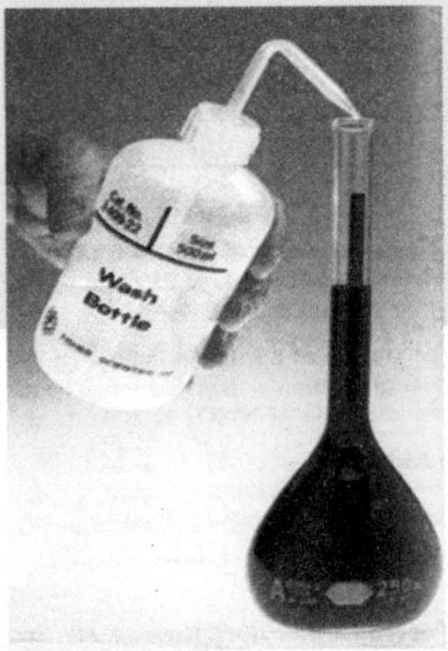

4 CHAPTER

Chemical Equations (II)

1. Limitations of the Hit and Trial Method. The *hit* and *trial* method is very useful for balancing simple chemical equations but has its own drawbacks also. These are:

(*i*) It takes a very long time to balance complicated equations in which the same element occurs in a number of compounds. This will be evident if you try to balance the following skeleton equation :

$$Zn + HNO_3 \rightarrow Zn(NO_3)_2 + N_2O + H_2O$$

(*ii*) In a number of cases the *mechanism of the reaction* is not clear. For example, if we write the action of chlorine on sodium hydroxide in the cold, we have :

$$NaOH + Cl_2 \rightarrow NaCl + NaClO + H_2O$$

Halite crystals (naturally occuring NaCl).

To equalize hydrogen atoms, multiply NaOH by 2. This gives us the balanced equation

$$2NaOH + Cl_2 \rightarrow NaCl + NaClO + H_2O$$

It is clear that balancing of the equation is very easy but the mechanism of the reaction as to how chlorine gas, which is not an acid can react with NaOH—an alkali, to give NaCl and NaClO (salts of hydrochloric acid and hypochlorous acid respectively) is not clear.

2. Partial Equations Method. In all such cases as given above, balancing can be more easily done by supposing the complex reaction to take place in steps, writing equations for these individual steps and finally adding them up. This is known as the method of *partial equations*. Balancing such equations by this method will illustrate its utility.

Metal crystals growing on zinc in lead nitrate solution.

Example 1. The reaction between zinc and dilute nitric acid to give zinc nitrate, nitrous oxide and water is supposed to be completed in the following steps:

(*a*) First dil. HNO_3 reacts with zinc to yield zinc nitrate and nascent hydrogen.

(*b*) The nascent hydrogen obtained in the first step reduces nitric acid to nitrous oxide and water. Products like nascent hydrogen which do not appear in the final products are known as **Intermediate Products.**

Writing simple equations for the two steps and adding them in such a way that the intermediate products (nascent hydrogen in the above case) cancel, we shall get the desired equation. To equalize nascent hydrogen atoms, multiply the first equation by 4. On adding, the nascent hydrogen atoms cancel each other, so that we have:

$$Zn + 2HNO_3 \rightarrow Zn(NO_3)_2 + 2H] \times 4$$
$$2HNO_3 + 8H \rightarrow N_2O + 5H_2O$$
$$\overline{4Zn + 10HNO_3 \rightarrow 4Zn(NO_3)_2 + N_2O + 5H_2O}$$

Example 2. Action of chlorine on cold caustic soda solution is supposed to be completed in the following three steps:

(*a*) Chlorine reacts with water to yield hydrochloric acid and hypochlorous acid.

(*b*) Hydrochloric acid produced in (*a*) reacts with NaOH to give NaCl and water.

(*c*) Hypochlorous acid produced in (*a*) reacts with NaOH to yield sodium hypochlorite and water.

Writing simple equation for these steps and adding them in such a way that the intermediate products (HCl and HClO in this ease) cancel, we shall have the desired equation

$$Cl_2 + H_2O \rightarrow HCl + HClO$$
$$HCl + NaOH \rightarrow NaCl + H_2O$$
$$HClO + NaOH \rightarrow NaClO + H_2O$$
$$\overline{Cl_2 + 2NaOH \rightarrow NaCl + NaClO + H_2O}$$

Example 3. Oxidation of lead sulphide by ozone is supposed to be completed in the following two steps :

(*a*) First ozone decomposes to give oxygen gas (molecular) and nascent oxygen (atomic).

(*b*) The nascent oxygen oxidises lead sulphide to lead sulphate.

Writing simple equations for the two steps and adding them in such a way that the *intermediate products* (nascent oxygen here) cancel, we get the desired equation as :

$$O_3 \rightarrow O_2 + O] \times 4$$
$$PbS + 4O \rightarrow PbSO_4$$
$$\overline{PbS + 4O_3 \rightarrow PbSO_4 + 4O_2}$$

Example 4. Liberation of iodine from potassium iodide by hydrogen peroxide is supposed to be completed in the following two steps :

(*a*) H_2O_2 decomposes to give water + nascent oxygen.

(*b*) Nascent oxygen produced in step (*a*) oxidises potassium iodide in presence of water to iodine and potassium hydroxide.

Writing simple equations for the two steps and adding in such a way that the *intermediate products* (nascent oxygen and water here) cancel, we get the desired equation as

The lilac colour indicates that the compound in the flame contains potassium.

$$H_2O_2 \rightarrow H_2O + O$$
$$2KI + H_2O + O \rightarrow 2KOH + I_2$$
$$\overline{2KI + H_2O_2 \rightarrow 2KOH + I_2}$$

Example 5. Oxidation of ferrous sulphate, H_2S or sulphur dioxide by acidified potassium permanganate is supposed to be completed in the following two steps :

(*a*) Potassium permanganate reacts with sulphuric acid to give potassium sulphate, manganous sulphate, water and nascent oxygen.

(*b*) Nascent oxygen obtained in step (*a*) oxidises ferrous sulphate, hydrogen sulphide or sulphur dioxide to the corresponding oxidation products: ferric sulphate, sulphur and sulphuric acid respectively.

Aqueous potassium permanganate is frequently used as an oxidizing agent.

Writing simple equations of the two steps separately in each case and then adding the partial equations in such a way that the *Intermediate products* cancel, we get three different equations:

(*i*) *For ferrous sulphate + acidified $KMnO_4$.*

$$2KMnO_4 + 3H_2SO_4 \rightarrow K_2SO_4 + 2MnSO_4 + 3H_2O + 5O$$

$$2FeSO_4 + H_2SO_4 + O \rightarrow Fe_2(SO_4)_3 + H_2O] \times 5$$

$$2KMnO_4 + 8H_2SO_4 + 10FeSO_4 \rightarrow K_2SO_4 + 2MnSO_4 + 5Fe_2(SO_4)_3 + 8H_2O$$

(*ii*) *For hydrogen sulphide + acidified $KMnO_4$.*

$$2KMnO_4 + 3H_2SO_4 \rightarrow K_2SO_4 + 2MnSO_4 + 3H_2O + 5O$$

$$H_2S + O \rightarrow H_2O + S] \times 5$$

$$2KMnO_4 + 3H_2SO_4 + 5H_2S \rightarrow K_2SO_4 + 2MnSO_4 + 8H_2O + 5S$$

(*iii*) *For sulphur dioxide + acidified $KMnO_4$.*

$$2KMnO_4 + 3H_2SO_4 \rightarrow K_2SO_4 + 2MnSO_4 + 3H_2O + 5O$$

$$SO_2 + O + H_2O \rightarrow H_2SO_4] \times 5$$

$$2KMnO_4 + 5SO_2 + 2H_2O \rightarrow K_2SO_4 + 2MnSO_4 + 2H_2SO_4$$

TEST YOUR UNDERSTANDING

Fill in the blanks in the following :

(*i*) In a complicated equation the same element occurs in a ....

(*ii*) It takes a long time to balance .... by hit and trial method.

(*iii*) A complicated reaction is supposed to occur in two or more............... A chemical equation is written for each .... and balanced by .... method. These .... equations are termed .... equations. These are added in such a way that the intermediate products ....

(*iv*) An intermediate product is one which does not appear in the ....

(*v*) Reaction between chlorine and caustic soda is supposed to proceed in .... steps involving .... and .... as intermediate products.

(*vi*) Oxidation of lead sulphide by ozone is supposed to proceed in .... steps. In the first step ozone decomposes to give nascent oxygen which oxidises PbS to .... in the second step. These two .... are added in such a way that .... being intermediate product cancels.

(*vii*) Similar two steps which explain the oxidation of KI by H_2O_2 are ....

(*viii*) Oxidation of H_2S by acidified $KMnO_4$ is supposed to proceed in the following two stages :

(*a*) Reaction between $KMnO_4$ and .... to produce .... + ... + ... + nascent oxygen.

(*b*) H_2S .... → .... + ... }

To get the final equation, the .... equation is multiplied by .... and added to the .... equation.

KEY

(*i*) number of compounds;
(*ii*) a complicated equation;
(*iii*) steps, step, hit and trial, step, partial, cancel;
(*iv*) final products;
(*v*) two, HCl, HClO;
(*vi*) two, $PbSO_4$, partial equations, nascent oxygen;
(*vii*) see text.
(*viii*) (*a*) H_2SO_4, K_2SO_4, $MnSO_4$, H_2O ;
(*b*) O, H_2O, S, second, 5, first.

EXERCISES

I. Write down in the language of chemistry the following partial equations written in words where the intermediate products are written in *italics*.

(*a*) Equations regarding oxidising properties of ozone

(*i*) Ozone → Oxygen + *Nascent oxygen*

Lead sulphide + *Nascent oxygen* → Lead sulphate

Lead sulphide + Ozone → Lead sulphate + Oxygen

(*ii*) Ozone → Oxygen + *Nascent oxygen*

Potassium iodide + *Nascent oxygen* + Water→ Potassium hydroxide + Iodine

---

Potassium iodide + *ozone* + Water → Potassium hydroxide + Iodine

(*iii*) Ozone → Oxygen + *Nascent oxygen*

Potassium manganate + *Nascent Oxygen* + Water → Potassium permanganate + Potassium hydroxide

---

Potassium manganate + Ozone + Water → Potassium permanganate Potassiumhydroxide + Oxygen

(*iv*) Ozone → Oxygen + *Nascent oxygen*

Potassium ferrocyanide + *Nascent oxygen* + Water → Potassiumferricyanide + Potassium hydroxide

---

Potassium ferrocyanide + Oxone + Water Potassium ferricyanide + Potassiumhydroxide + Oxygen

(*b*) Equations regarding oxidising properties of H_2O_2.

The two stages in which reaction takes place are indicated below. The students should write their skeleton equations for each step and then add the two in such a way that nascent oxygen which is an intermediate product, cancels.

1st step *which is common for all the reactions:*

Hydrogen peroxide → Water + *Nascent oxygen.*

2nd step *which is different for different reactions :*

(1) Lead sulphide + *Nascent oxygen* → Lead sulphate.

(2) Potassium iodide + Water + *Nascent oxygen* → Potassium hydroxide + Iodine.

(3) Potassium sulphite + *Nascent oxygen* → Potassium sulphate.

(4) Ferrous sulphate + Sulphuric acid + *Nascent oxygen* → Ferric sulphate + Water.

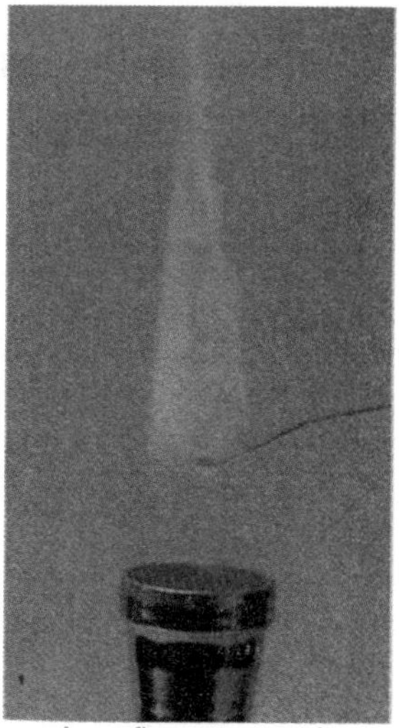

A confirmatory test for potassium.

(5) Arsenious acid + *Nascent oxygen* → Arsenic acid.

(6) Potassium nitrite + *Nascent oxygen* → Potassiumnitrate.

(*c*) Equations regarding the oxidising reactions of acidified potassium permanganate. Here again the students will write their own skeleton equations of the two steps indicated below, involved in each reaction as done in I (*b*).

A sample of potassium metal.

1st step *which is common for all the reactions :*

Potassium permanganate + Sulphuric acid → Potassium sulphate+Manganous sulphate + Water + *Nascent oxygen.*

2nd step *which is different for different reactions* :

(*i*) Hydrogen sulphide + *Nascent oxygen* → Sulphur + Water.

(*ii*) Sulphur dioxide + *Nascent oxygen* + Water → Sulphuric acid

(*iii*) Ferrous sulphate + *Nascent oxygen* + Sulphuric acid →Ferric sulphate + Water

(*iv*) Nitrous acid + *Nascent oxygen* → Nitric acid.

(*v*) Oxalic acid + *Nascent oxygen* → Carbon dioxide + Water.

(*vi*) Hydrogen peroxide + *Nascent oxygen* → Water + Oxygen.

(*vii*) Potassium iodide + Sulphuric acid + *Nascent oxygen* → Potassium bisulphate + Iodine + Water.

(*viii*) Sodium sulphite + *Nascent oxygen* → Sodium sulphate.

(*d*) Equations regarding oxidizing reactions of acidified potassium dichromate. Proceed in the same manner as suggested above in the case of $KMnO_4$.

Potassium dichromate (VI) solution.

1st step *which is common for all the reactions:*

Potassium dichromate + Sulphuric acid → Potassium sulphate + Chromium sulphate + Water + *Nascent oxygen.*

2nd step *which is different for individual reactions:*

1. Ferrous sulphate + Sulphuric acid + *Nascent oxygen* → Ferric sulphate + Water.
2. Sodium sulphite + *Nascent oxygen* → Sodium sulphate.
3. Sulphur dioxide + *Nascent oxygen* + Water → Sulphuric acid

4. Potassium iodide + Sulphuric acid + *Nascent oxygen*
→ Potassium hydrogen sulphate + Iodine + Water.
5. Hydrobromic acid + *Nascent oxygen* → Bromine + Water.
6. Hydrogen sulphide + *Nascent oxygen* → Sulphur + Water.
7. Stannous chloride + Hydrochloric acid + *Nascent oxygen*
→ Stannic chloride + Water.
8. Oxalic acid + *Nascent oxygen* → Carbon dioxide + Water.
9. Nitrous acid + *Nascent oxygen* → Nitric acid.

(*e*) Equations regarding the oxidising reactions of Chlorine. The two stages in which each reaction takes place are indicated below. The students should write their own skeleton equations for the two steps and proceed as before.

1st step *which is common for all the reactions* :

Chlorine + Water → Hydrochloric acid + *Nascent oxygen.*

2nd step *which is different for different reactions* :

(*i*) Ferrous sulphate + Sulphuric Acid + *Nascent oxygen*
→ Ferric sulphate + Water.

(*ii*) Hydrogen sulphide + *Nascent oxygen* → Sulphur + Water.

(*iii*) Sodium sulphite + *Nascent oxygen* → Sodium sulphate.

(*iv*) Sodium thiosulphate + *Nascent oxygen* → Sodium sulphate + Sulphur.

(*f*) Equations regarding the oxidising reactions of Bromine. The two stages in which each reaction proceeds are given below:

1st step *which is common for all the reactions :*

Bromine + Water → Hydrobromic acid + *Nascent oxygen.*

2nd step *which is different for different reactions:*

(*i*) Hydrogen sulphide + *Nascent oxygen* → Sulphur + Water.

(*ii*) Sulphur dioxide + *Nascent oxygen* + Water → Sulphuric acid.

(*iii*) Sodium Sulphite + *Nascent oxygen* → Sodium Sulphate

(*iv*) Sodium thiosulphate + *Nascent oxygen* → Sodium sulphate + Sulphur.

(*v*) Sodium arsenite + *Nascent oxygen* → Sodium arsenate.

Bromine is a dark red liquid.

(g) Equations regarding oxidising reactions of Iodine. Iodine resembles chlorine and bromine in its oxidising reactions. The two stages in which each reaction proceeds are indicated below :

1st step *which is common for all the reactions :*

Iodine + Water → Hydriodic acid + Nascent oxygen.

2nd step *which is different for different reactions:*

(*i*) Hydrogen sulphide + *Nascent oxygen* → Sulphur + Water.

(*ii*) Sulphur dioxide + *Nascent oxygen* + water → Sulphuric acid.

(*iii*) Potassium nitrite + *Nascent oxygen* → Potassium nitrate.

(*iv*) Sodium sulphite + *Nascent oxygen* → Sodium sulphate.

(*v*) Sodium arsenite + *Nascent oxygen* → Sodium arsenate.

Native sulphur. Elemental sulphur is deposited at the edges of some hot springs and geysers.

(*h*) Equations regarding the oxidising reactions of nitrous acid. On account of its instability, nitrous acid acts as an oxidising agent. It oxidises H_2S, KI and $SnCl_2$.

In the **first step** nitrous acid decomposes to liberate nascent oxgyen according to the equation:

Nitrous acid → Nitric oxide + Water + *Nascent oxygen.*

In the **second step**, various substances are oxidised by nascent oxygen to corresponding oxidation products according to the following equations:

1. Hydrogen sulphide + *Nascent oxygen* → Sulphur + Water.
2. Sulphur dioxide + *Nascent oxygen* + Water → Sulphuric acid.
3. Potassium iodide + Water + *Nascent oxygen* → Potassium hydroxide + Iodine.
4. Stannous chloride + Hydrochloric acid + *Nascent oxygen* → Stannic chloride + Water.

(*i*) Equations regarding reactions of conc. nitric acid on non-metals–S, C, P, I_2 and metalloids—As, Sb.

1st Step. Nitric acid decomposes to give out nascent oxygen according to the following equation:

Nitric acid → Nitrogen dioxide + Water—*Nascent oxygen.*

2nd Step. Nascent oxygen obtained in the first step, oxidizes the non-metals and metalloids to the corresponding oxyacids as given below:

1. Sulphur + *Nascent oxygen* + Water → Sulphuric acid.
2. Carbon + *Nascent oxygen* + Water → Carbonic acid.
3. Phosphorus + *Nascent oxygen* + Water → Phosphoric acid.

4. Iodine + *Nascent oxygen* + Water → Iodic acid.
5. Arsenic + *Nascent oxygen* + Water → Arsenic acid.
6. Antimony + *Nascent oxygen* + Water → Antimonic acid.
7. Tin is not a metalloid but resembles them in this reaction as given below:

Tin + *Nascent oxygen* + Water → Metastannic acid

(*j*) Equations regarding action of nitric acid on active metals.

In the **first step,** nitric acid reacts with the metal to give the nitrate of the metal + *Nascent hydrogen.*

In the **second step**, the nascent hydrogen obtained in the first step reduces nitric acid to N_2O, NO, NO_2, or NH_4NO_3 depending upon

(*i*) the nature of the metal, (*ii*) dilution of the acid, and (*iii*) temperature.

Both the steps are indicated below for various reactions. Translate them into language of chemistry and add in such a way that the intermediate products (nascent hydrogen in this case) cancel.

1. Zinc + dil. Nitric acid → Zinc nitrate + *Nascent Hydrogen*
   Nitric acid + *Nascent Hydrogen*→ *Nitrous oxide* + Water
2. Zinc + V. dil. Nitric acid → Zinc nitrate + *Nascent hydrogen*
   Nitric acid + *Nascent hydrogen* → Ammonium nitrate + Water
3. Zinc + conc. Nitric acid → Zinc nitrate + *Nascent hydrogen*
   Nitric acid + *Nascent hydrogen* → Nitrogen dioxide + Water
4. Tin + dil. Nitric acid → Stannous nitrate + *Nascent hydrogen*
   Nitric acid + *Nascent hydrogen*→ Ammonium nitrate + Water
5. Iron + dil. Nitric acid → Ferrous nitrate + *Nascent hydrogen*
   Nitric acid + *Nascent hydrogen* → Ammonium nitrate + Water
6. Iron + Moderately conc. Nitric acid → Ferric nitrate + Nascent hydrogen
   Nitric acid + *Nascent hydrogen* → Nitrogen dioxide + Water

(*k*) Equations regarding action of nitric acid on less active metals.

In the **first step**, nitric acid oxidises the metal to its oxide and is itself reduced to NO or NO_2 depending upon (*i*) dilution of the acid and (*ii*) temperature.

In the **second step**, metal oxide obtained in the first step reacts with nitric acid to give metal nitrate and water.

Both the steps are indicated below for various reactions. Translate them into language of chemistry and add in such a way that the intermediate products (nascent hydrogen in this case) cancel.

1. Copper + dil. Nitric acid → *Cupric oxide* + *Nitric oxide* + *Water*
   Cupric oxide + Nitric acid → Copper nitrate + Water

2. Copper + Nitric acid (conc.) →
Cupric oxide + Nitrogen dioxide + Water
Cupric oxide + nitric acid →
Copper nitrate + Water
3. Silver + Nitric acid (dil.) →
Silver oxide + Nitric oxide + Water
Silver oxide + Nitric acid →
Silver nitrate + Water
4. Lead + Nitric acid (dil.) →
Lead oxide + Nitric oxide + Water
Lead oxide + Nitric acid →
Lead nitrate + Water

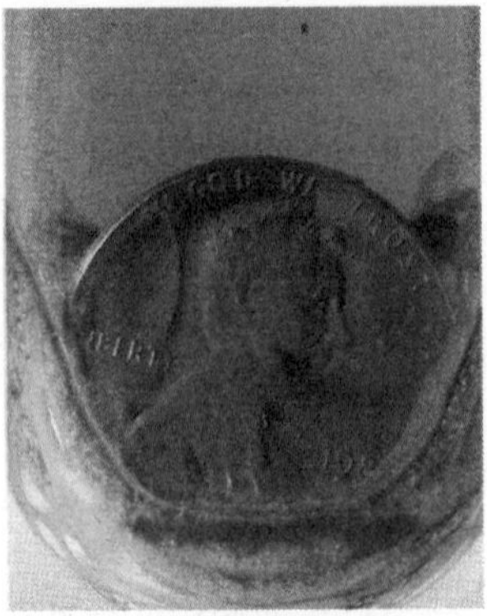

Copper metal reacts with nitric acid (HNO_3) to yield the brown gas NO_2.

5. Lead + Nitric acid (conc.) →
Lead oxide + Nitrogen dioxide + Water
Lead oxide + Nitric acid → Lead nitrate + Water
6. Mercury + Nitric acid (dil.) → Mercurous oxide + Nitric oxide + Water
Mercurous oxide + Nitric acid → Mercurous nitrate + Water
7. Mercury + Nitric acid (conc.) → Mercuric oxide + Nitrogen dioxide + Water
Mercuric oxide + Nitric acid → Mercuric nitrate + Water

II. Translate the following chemical equations for action of heat on various compounds, into language of chemistry and balance them by any of the two methods described earlier.

(1) Potassium nitrate → Potassium nitrite + Oxygen.
(2) Sodium nitrate → Sodium nitrite + Oxygen.
(3) Ammonium nitrate → Nitrous oxide + Water
(4) Lead nitrate → Lead oxide + Nitrogen dioxide + Oxygen.
(Similarly write for other heavy metal nitrates)
(5) Mercuric nitrate → Mercury + Nitrogen dioxide + Oxygen.
(6) Ferrous sulphate → Ferric oxide + Sulphur dioxide + Sulphur trioxide.
(7) Ferric sulphate → Ferric oxide + Sulphur trioxide.
(8) Sodium bisulphate → Sodium pyrosulphate + Water
(9) Potassium chlorate → Potassium chloride + Oxygen.
(10) Potassium permanganate → Potassium manganate + Manganese dioxide + Oxygen
(11) Cupric chloride → Cuprous chloride + Chlorine
(12) Mono-sodium dihydrogen phosphate → Sodium metaphosphate + Water

(13) Sodium ammonium hydrogen phosphate → Sodium metaphosphate + Ammonia + Water

(14) Disodium hydrogen phosphate → Sodium pyrophosphate + Water

(15) Magnesium ammonium phosphate → Magnesium pyrophosphate + Ammonia

A number of minerals contain the carbonate ion. A very common is calcium carbonate ($CaCO_3$), the main constituent of limestone and of stalactites and stalagmites.

(16) Calcium carbonate → Calcium oxide + Carbon dioxide

(17) Copper carbonate → Copper oxide + Carbon dioxide
(Similarly write for other heavy metal carbonates)

(18) Calcium bicarbonate → Calcium oxide + Carbon dioxide + Water

(19) Sodium bicarbonate →Sodium carbonate + Carbon dioxide + Water

(20) Ammonium dichromate → Chromium oxide + Nitrogen + Water

ANSWERS

I. (*a*) (*i*) $O_3 \rightarrow [O_2 + O] \times 4$

$$PbS + 4O \rightarrow PbSO_4$$

$$PbS + 4O_3 \rightarrow PbSO_4 + 4O_2$$

(*ii*) $O_3 \rightarrow O_2 + O$

$$2KI + O + H_2O \rightarrow 2KOH + I_2$$

$$2KI + O_3 + H_2O \rightarrow 2KOH + O_2 + I_2$$

(*iii*) $O_3 \rightarrow O_2 + O$

$$2K_2MnO_4 + O + H_2O \rightarrow 2KMnO_4 + 2KOH$$

$$2K_2MnO_4 + H_2O + O_3 \rightarrow 2KMnO_4 + 2KOH + O_2$$

(*iv*) $O_3 \rightarrow O_2 + O$

$$\frac{2K_4Fe(CN)_6 + H_2O + O \rightarrow 2K_3Fe(CN)_6 + 2KOH}{2K_4Fe(CN)_6 + O_3 + H_2O \rightarrow 2K_3Fe(CN)_6 + 2KOH + O_2}$$

(*b*) (1) $H_2O_2 \rightarrow H_2O + O] \times 4$

$$\frac{PbS + 4O \rightarrow PbSO_4}{PbS + 4H_2O_2 \rightarrow PbSO_4 + 4H_2O}$$

(2) $H_2O_2 \rightarrow H_2O + O$

$$\frac{2KI + H_2O + O \rightarrow 2KOH + I_2}{2KI + H_2O_2 \rightarrow 2KOH + I_2}$$

(3) $H_2O_2 \rightarrow H_2O + O$

$$\frac{K_2SO_3 + O \rightarrow K_2SO_4}{H_2O_2 + K_2SO_3 \rightarrow K_2SO_4 + H_2O}$$

(4) $H_2O_2 \rightarrow H_2O + O$

$$\frac{2FeSO_4 + H_2SO_4 + O \rightarrow Fe_2(SO_4)_3 + H_2O}{2FeSO_4 + H_2SO_4 + H_2O_2I \rightarrow Fe_2(SO_4)_3 + 2H_2O}$$

(5) $H_2O_2 \rightarrow H_2O + O$

$$\frac{H_3AsO_3 + O \rightarrow H_3AsO_4}{H_3AsO_3 + H_2O_2 \rightarrow H_3AsO_4 + H_2O}$$

(6) $H_2O_2 \rightarrow H_2O + O$

$$\frac{KNO_2 + O \rightarrow KNO_3}{KNO_2 + H_2O_2 \rightarrow KNO_3 + H_2O}$$

(*c*) (*i*) $2KMnO_4 + 3H_2SO_4 \rightarrow K_2SO_4 + 2MnSO_4 + 3H_2O + 5O$

$$\frac{H_2S + O \rightarrow H_2O + S] \times 5}{2KMnO_4 + 3H_2SO_4 + 5H_2S \rightarrow K_2SO_4 + 2MnSO_4 + 8H_2O + 5S}$$

(*ii*) $2KMnO_4 + 3H_2SO_4 \rightarrow K_2SO_4 + 2MnSO_4 + 3H_2O + 5O$

$$\frac{SO_2 + H_2O + O \rightarrow H_2SO_4] \times 5}{2KMnO_4 + 5SO_4 + 2H_2O \rightarrow K_2SO_4 + 2MnSO_4 + 2H_2SO_4}$$

(*iii*) $2KMnO_4 + 3H_2SO_4 \rightarrow K_2SO_4 + 2MnSO_4 + 3H_2O + 5O$

$2FeSO_4 + H_2SO_4 + O \rightarrow Fe_2(SO_4)_3 + H_2O] \times 5$

$$2KMnO_4 + 8H_2SO_4 + 10FeSO_4 \rightarrow 5Fe_2(SO_4)_3 + K_2SO_4 + 2MnSO_4 + 8H_2O$$

(*iv*) $2KMnO_4 + 3H_2SO_4 \rightarrow K_2SO_4 + 2MnSO_4 + 3H_2O + 5O$

$HNO_2 + O \rightarrow HNO_3] \times 5$

$$2KMnO_4 + 3H_2SO_4 + 5HNO_2 \rightarrow K_2SO_4 + 2MnSO_4 + 5HNO_3 + 3H_2O$$

(*v*) $2KMnO_4 + 3H_2SO_4 \rightarrow K_2SO_4 + 2MnSO_4 + 3H_2O + 5O$

$(COOH)_2 + O \rightarrow 2CO_2 + H_2O] \times 5$

$$2KMnO_4 + 3H_2SO_4 + 5(COOH)_2 \rightarrow K_2SO_4 + 2MnSO_4 + 8H_2O + 10CO_2$$

(*vi*) $2KMnO_4 + 3H_2SO_4 \rightarrow K_2SO_4 + 2MnSO_4 + 3H_2O + 5O$

$H_2O_2 + O \rightarrow H_2O + O_2] \times 5$

$$2KMnO_4 + 3H_2SO_4 + 5H_2O_2 \rightarrow K_2SO_4 + 2MnSO_4 + 8H_2O + 5O_2$$

(*vii*) $2KMnO_4 + 3H_2SO_4 \rightarrow K_2SO_4 + 2MnSO_4 + 3H_2O + 5O$

$2KI + 2H_2SO_4 + O \rightarrow 2KHSO_4 + I_2 + H_2O] \times 5$

$$2KMnO_4 + 3H_2SO_4 + 10KI \rightarrow K_2SO_4 + 10KHSO_4 + 2MnSO_4 + 8H_2O + 5I_2$$

(*viii*) $2KMnO_4 + 3H_2SO_4 \rightarrow K_2SO_4 + 2MnSO_4 + 3H_2O + 5O$

$Na_2SO_3 + O \rightarrow Na_2SO_4] \times 5$

$$2KMnO_4 + 3H_2SO_4 + 5Na_2SO_3 \rightarrow K_2SO_4 + 2MnSO_4 + 3H_2O + 5Na_2SO_4$$

(***d***) (1) $K_2Cr_2O_7 + 4H_2SO_4 \rightarrow K_2SO_4 + Cr_2(SO_4)_3 + 4H_2O + 3O$

$2FeSO_4 + H_2SO_4 + O \rightarrow Fe_2(SO_4)_3 + H_2O] \times 3$

$$K_2Cr_2O_7 + 7H_2SO_4 + 6FeSO_4 \rightarrow K_2SO_4 + Cr_2(SO_4)_3 + 3Fe_2(SO_4)_3 + 7H_2O$$

(2) $K_2Cr_2O_7 + 4H_2SO_4 \rightarrow K_2SO_4 + Cr_2(SO_4)_3 + 4H_2O + 3O$

$Na_2SO_3 + O \rightarrow Na_2SO_4] \times 3$

$$K_2Cr_2O_7 + 4H_2SO_4 + 3Na_2SO_3 \rightarrow K_2SO_4 + Cr_2(SO_4)_3 + 3Na_2SO_4 + 4H_2O$$

(3)

$$K_2Cr_2O_7 + 4H_2SO_4 \rightarrow K_2SO_4 + Cr_2(SO_4)_3 + 4H_2O + 3O$$

$$SO_2 + H_2O + O \rightarrow H_2SO_4] \times 3$$

$$K_2Cr_2O_7 + H_2SO_4 + 3SO_2 \rightarrow K_2SO_4 + Cr_2(SO_4)_3 + H_2O$$

(4)

$$K_2Cr_2O_7 + 4H_2SO_4 \rightarrow K_2SO_4 + Cr_2(SO_4)_3 + 4H_2O + 3O$$

$$2KI + 2H_2SO_4 + O \rightarrow 2KHSO_4 + I_2 + H_2O] \times 3$$

$$K_2Cr_2O_7 + 10H_2SO_4 + 6KI \rightarrow K_2SO_4 + Cr_2(SO_4)_3 + 6KHSO_4 + 3I_2 + 7H_2O$$

(5)

$$K_2Cr_2O_7 + 4H_2SO_4 \rightarrow K_2SO_4 + Cr_2(SO_4)_3 + 4H_2O + 3O$$

$$2HBr + O \rightarrow H_2O + Br_2] \times 3$$

$$K_2Cr_2O_7 + 4H_2SO_4 + 6HBr \rightarrow K_2SO_4 + Cr_2(SO_4)_3 + 7H_2O + 3Br_2$$

(6)

$$K_2Cr_2O_7 + 4H_2SO_4 \rightarrow K_2SO_4 + Cr_2(SO_4)_3 + 4H_2O + 3O$$

$$H_2S + O \rightarrow H_2O + S] \times 3$$

$$K_2Cr_2O_7 + 4H_2SO_4 + 3H_2S \rightarrow K_2SO_4 + Cr_2(SO_4)_3 + 7H_2O + 3S$$

(7)

$$K_2Cr_2O_7 + 4H_2SO_4 \rightarrow K_2SO_4 + Cr_2(SO_4)_3 + 4H_2O + 3O$$

$$SnCl_2 + 2HCl + O \rightarrow SnCl_4 + H_2O] \times 3$$

$$K_2Cr_2O_7 + 4H_2SO_4 + 3SnCl_2 + 6HCl \rightarrow K_2SO_4 + Cr_2(SO_4)_3 + 7H_2O + 3SnCl_4$$

(8)

$$K_2Cr_2O_7 + 4H_2SO_4 \rightarrow K_2SO_4 + Cr_2(SO_4)_3 + 4H_2O + 3O$$

$$(COOH)_2 + O \rightarrow 2CO_2 + H_2O] \times 3$$

$$K_2Cr_2O_7 + 4H_2SO_4 + 3(COOH)_2 \rightarrow K_2SO_4 + Cr_2(SO_4)_3 + 6CO_2 + 7H_2O$$

(9)

$$K_2Cr_2O_7 + 4H_2SO_4 \rightarrow K_2SO_4 + Cr_2(SO_4)_3 + 4H_2O + 3O$$

$$HNO_2 + O \rightarrow HNO_3] \times 3$$

$$K_2Cr_2O_7 + 4H_2SO_4 + 3HNO_2 \rightarrow K_2SO_4 + Cr_2(SO_4)_3 + 4H_2O + 3HNO_3$$

(e) (*i*) $Cl_2 + H_2O \rightarrow 2HCl + O$

$$2FeSO_4 + H_2SO_4 + O \rightarrow Fe_2(SO_4)_3 + H_2O$$

$$2FeSO_2 + H_2SO_4 + Cl_2 \rightarrow Fe_2(SO_4)_3 + 2HCl$$

(*ii*) $Cl_2 + H_2O \rightarrow 2HCl + O$

$$H_2S + O \rightarrow S + H_2O$$

$$H_2S + Cl_2 \rightarrow 2HCl + S$$

(*iii*) $Cl_2 + H_2O \rightarrow 2HCl + O$

$$Na_2SO_3 + O \rightarrow Na_2SO_4$$

$$Na_2SO_3 + Cl_2 + H_2O \rightarrow Na_2SO_4 + 2HCl$$

(*iv*) $Cl_2 + H_2O \rightarrow 2HCl + O$

$$Na_2S_2O_3 + O \rightarrow Na_2SO_4 + S$$

$$Na_2S_2O_3 + Cl_2 + H_2O \rightarrow Na_2SO_4 + S + 2HCl$$

(f) (*i*) $Br_2 + H_2O \rightarrow 2HBr + O$

$$H_2S + O \rightarrow S + H_2O$$

$$Br_2 + H_2S \rightarrow 2HBr + S$$

(*ii*) $Br_2 + H_2O \rightarrow 2HBr + O$

$$SO_2 + O + H_2O \rightarrow H_2SO_4$$

$$Br_2 + SO_2 + 2H_2O \rightarrow 2HBr + H_2SO_4$$

(*iii*) $Br_2 + H_2O \rightarrow 2HBr + O$

$$Na_2SO_3 + O \rightarrow Na_2SO_4$$

$$Na_2SO_3 + Br_2 + H_2O \rightarrow Na_2SO_4 + 2HBr$$

(*iv*) $Br_2 + H_2O \rightarrow 2HBr + O$

$$Na_2S_2O_3 + O \rightarrow Na_2SO_4 + S$$

$$Na_2S_2O_3 + Br_2 + H_2O \rightarrow Na_2SO_4 + S + 2HBr$$

(*v*) $Br_2 + H_2O \rightarrow 2HBr + O$

$$Na_3AsO_3 + O \rightarrow Na_3AsO_4$$

$$Na_3AsO_3 + Br_2 + H_2O \rightarrow Na_3AsO_4 + 2HBr$$

(g) (*i*) $I_2 + H_2O \rightarrow 2HI + O$

$$H_2S + O \rightarrow S + H_2O$$

$$H_2S + I_2 \rightarrow S + 2HI$$

(ii) $$I_2 + H_2O \rightarrow 2HI + O$$
$$SO_2 + O + H_2O \rightarrow H_2SO_4$$
$$\overline{I_2 + SO_2 + 2H_2O \rightarrow H_2SO_4 + 2HI}$$

(iii) $$I_2 + H_2O \rightarrow 2HI + O$$
$$KNO_2 + O \rightarrow KNO_3$$
$$\overline{KNO_2 + I_2 + H_2O \rightarrow KNO_3 + 2HI}$$

(iv) $$I_2 + H_2O \rightarrow 2HI + O$$
$$Na_2SO_3 + O \rightarrow Na_2SO_4$$
$$\overline{I_2 + Na_2SO_3 + H_2O \rightarrow Na_2SO_4 + 2HI}$$

(v) $$I_2 + H_2O \rightarrow 2HI + O$$
$$Na_3AsO_3 + O \rightarrow Na_3AsO_4$$
$$\overline{Na_3AsO_3 + I_2 + H_2O \rightarrow Na_3AsO_4 + 2HI}$$

(h) (1) $$2HNO_2 \rightarrow H_2O + 2NO + O$$
$$H_2S + O \rightarrow H_2O + S$$
$$\overline{2HNO_2 + H_2S \rightarrow 2NO + 2H_2O + S}$$

(2) $$2HNO_2 \rightarrow H_2O + 2NO + O$$
$$SO_2 + H_2O + O \rightarrow H_2SO_4$$
$$\overline{SO_2 + 2HNO_2 \rightarrow H_2SO_4 + 2NO}$$

(3) $$2HNO_2 \rightarrow H_2O + 2NO + O$$
$$2KI + H_2O + O \rightarrow 2KOH + I_2$$
$$\overline{2HNO_2 + 2KI \rightarrow 2KOH + I_2 + 2NO}$$

(4) $$2HNO_2 \rightarrow H_2O + 2NO + O$$
$$SnCl_2 + 2HCl + O \rightarrow SnCl_4 + H_2O$$
$$\overline{SnCl_2 + 2HCl + 2HNO_2 \rightarrow SnCl_4 + 2NO + 2H_2O}$$

(i) (1) $$2HNO_3 \rightarrow 2NO_2 + H_2O + O] \times 3$$
$$S + 3O + H_2O \rightarrow H_2SO_4$$
$$\overline{S + 6HNO_3 \rightarrow H_2SO_4 + 6NO_2 + 2H_2O}$$

(2) $2HNO_3 \rightarrow 2NO_2 + H_2O + O] \times 2$

$$C + 2O + H_2O \rightarrow H_2CO_3$$

$$C + 4HNO_3 \rightarrow H_2CO_3 + 4NO_2 + H_2$$

(3) $2HNO_3 \rightarrow 2NO_2 + H_2O + O] \times 5$

$$2P + 5O + 3H_2O \rightarrow 2H_3PO_4$$

$$2P + 10HNO_3 \rightarrow 2H_3PO_4 + 10NO_2 + 2H_2O$$

or $P + 5HNO_3 \rightarrow H_3PO_4 + 5NO_2 + 4H_2O$

(4) $2HNO_3 \rightarrow 2NO_2 + H_2O + O] \times 5$

$$I_2 + 5O + H_2O \rightarrow 2HIO_3$$

$$I_2 + 10HNO_3 \rightarrow 2HIO_3 + 10NO_2 + 4H_2O$$

(5) $2HNO_3 \rightarrow 2NO_2 + H_2O + O] \times 5$

$$2As + 5O + 3H_2O \rightarrow 2H_3AsO_4$$

$$2As + 10HNO_3 \rightarrow 2H_3AsO_4 + 10NO_2 + 2H_2O$$

or $As + 5HNO_3 \rightarrow H_3AsO_4 + 5NO_2 + 2H_2O$

(6) $2HNO_3 \rightarrow 2NO_2 + H_2O + O] \times 5$

$$2Sb + 5O + 3H_2O \rightarrow 2H_3SbO_4$$

$$2Sb + 10HNO_3 \rightarrow 2H_3SbO_4 + 10NO_2 + 2H_2O$$

or $Sb + 5HNO_3 \rightarrow H_3SbO_4 + 5NO_2 + H_2O$

(7) $2HNO_3 \rightarrow 2NO_2 + H_2O + O] \times 2$

$$Sn + 2O + H_2O \rightarrow H_2SnO_3$$

$$Sn + 4HNO_3 \rightarrow H_2SnO_3 + 4NO_2 + H_2O$$

(*j*) (1) $Zn + 2HNO_3 \rightarrow Zn(NO_3)_2 + 2H] \times 4$

$$2HNO_3 + 8H \rightarrow N_2O + 5H_2O$$

$$4Zn + 10HNO_3 \rightarrow 4Zn(NO_3)_2 + 5H_2O + N_2O$$

(2) $Zn + 2HNO_3 \rightarrow Zn(NO_3)_2 + 2H] \times 4$

$$2HNO_3 + 8H \rightarrow NH_4NO_3 + 3H_2O$$

$$4Zn + 10HNO_3 \rightarrow Zn(NO_3)_2 + NH_4NO_3 + 3H_2O$$

(3) $Zn + 2HNO_3 \rightarrow Zn(NO_3)_2 + 2H$

$HNO_3 + H \rightarrow NO_2 + H_2O] \times 2$

$Zn + 4HNO_3 \rightarrow Zn(NO_3)_2 + 2NO_2 + 2H_2O$

(4) $Sn + 2HNO_3 \rightarrow Sn(NO_3)_2 + 2H] \times 4$

$2HNO_3 + 8H \rightarrow NH_4NO_3 + 3H_2O$

$4Sn + 10HNO_3 \rightarrow 4Sn(NO_3)_2 + NH_4NO_3 + 3H_2O$

(5) $Fe + 2HNO_3 \rightarrow Fe(NO_3)_2 + 2H] \times 4$

$2HNO_3 + 8H \rightarrow NH_4NO_3 + 3H_2O$

$4Fe + 10HNO_3 \rightarrow 4Fe(NO_3)_2 + NH_4NO_3 + 3H_2O$

(6) $Fe + 3HNO_3 \rightarrow Fe(NO_3)_3 + 3H$

$HNO_3 + H \rightarrow H_2O + NO_2] \times 3$

$Fe + 6HNO_3 \rightarrow Fe(NO_3)_3 + 3NO_2 + 4H_2O$

(*k*) (1) $3Cu + 2HNO_3 \rightarrow 3CuO + 2NO + H_2O$

$CuO + 2HNO_3 \rightarrow Cu(NO_3)_2 + H_2O] \times 3$

$3Cu + 8HNO_3 \rightarrow 3Cu(NO_3)_2 + 2NO + 4H_2O$

(2) $Cu + 2HNO_3 \rightarrow CuO + 2NO + H_2O$

$CuO + 2HNO_3 \rightarrow Cu(NO_3)_2 + H_2O$

$Cu + 4HNO_3 \rightarrow Cu(NO_3)_2 + 2NO_2 + 2H_2O$

(3) $6Ag + 2HNO_3 \rightarrow 3Ag_2O + 2NO + H_2O$

$Ag_2O + 2HNO_3 \rightarrow 2AgNO_3 + H_2O] \times 3$

$6Ag + 8HNO_3 \rightarrow 6AgNO_3 + 2NO + 4H_2O$

or $3Ag + 4HNO_3 \rightarrow 3AgNO_3 + NO + 2H_2O$

(4) $3Pb + 2HNO_3 \rightarrow 3PbO + 2NO + H_2O$

$PbO + 2HNO_3 \rightarrow Pb(NO_3)_2 + H_2O] \times 3$

$3Pb + 8HNO_3 \rightarrow 3Pb(NO_3)_2 + 2NO + 4H_2O$

(5) $Pb + 2HNO_3 \rightarrow PbO + 2NO_2 + H_2O$

$$PbO + 2HNO_3 \rightarrow Pb(NO_3)_2 + H_2O$$

$$Pb + 4HNO_3 \rightarrow Pb(NO_3)_2 + 2NO_2 + 2H_2O$$

(6) $6Hg + 2HNO_3 \rightarrow 3Hg_2O + 2NO + H_2O$

$$Hg_2O + 2HNO_3 \rightarrow Hg_2(NO_3)_2 + H_2O] \times 3$$

$$6Hg + 8HNO_3 \rightarrow 3Hg_2(NO_3)_2 + 2NO + 4H_2O$$

(7) $Hg + 2HNO_3 \rightarrow HgO + 2NO_2 + H_2O$

$$HgO + 2HNO_3 \rightarrow Hg(NO_3)_2 + H_2O$$

$$Hg + 4HNO_3 \rightarrow Hg(NO_3)_2 + 2NO_2 + 2H_2O$$

II. 1. $2KNO_3 \rightarrow 2KNO_2 + O_2$

2. $2NaNO_3 \rightarrow 2NaNO_2 + O_2$

3. $NH_4NO_3 \rightarrow N_2O + 2H_2O$

4. $2Pb(NO_3)_2 \rightarrow 2PbO + 4NO_2 + O_2$

5. $Hg(NO_3)_2 \rightarrow Hg + 2NO_2 + O_2$

6. $2FeSO_4 \rightarrow Fe_2O_3 + SO_2 + SO_3$

7. $Fe_2(SO_4)_3 \rightarrow Fe_2O_3 + 3SO_3$

8. $2NaHSO_4 \rightarrow Na_2S_2O_7 + H_2O$

9. $2KClO_3 \rightarrow 3KCl + 3O_2$

10. $2KMnO_4 \rightarrow K_2MnO_4 + MnO_2 + O_2$

11. $2CuCl_2 \rightarrow 2CuCl + Cl_2$

12. $NaH_2PO_4 \rightarrow NaPO_3 + H_2O$

13. $NaNH_4HPO_4 \rightarrow NaPO_3 + NH_3 + H_2O$

14. $2Na_2HPO_4 \rightarrow Na_4P_2O_7 + H_2O$

15. $2MgNH_4PO_4 \rightarrow Mg_2P_2O_7 + 2NH_3 + H_2O$

16. $CaCO_3 \rightarrow CaO + CO_2$

17. $CuCO_3 \rightarrow CuO + CO_2$

18. $Ca(HCO_3)_2 \rightarrow CaO + 2CO_2 + H_2O$

19. $2NaHCO_3 \rightarrow Na_2CO_3 + CO_2 + H_2O$

20. $(NH_4)_2Cr_2O_7 \rightarrow Cr_2O_3 + N_2 + 4H_2O$

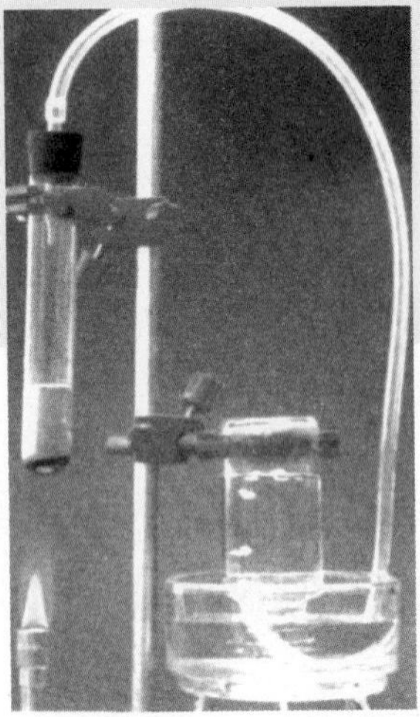

5
CHAPTER

Ionic Equations

1. Molecular and Ionic Equations. On adding silver nitrate solution to a sodium chloride solution we get a white precipitate of silver chloride. Sodium chloride (a salt) is produced on mixing sodium hydroxide and hydrochloric acid in equivalent proportion. These reactions are usually represented by the following chemical equations :

$$NaCl + AgNO_3 \rightarrow AgCl + NaNO_3$$
$$NaOH + HCl \rightarrow NaCl + H_2O$$

These equations are termed *molecular equations*.

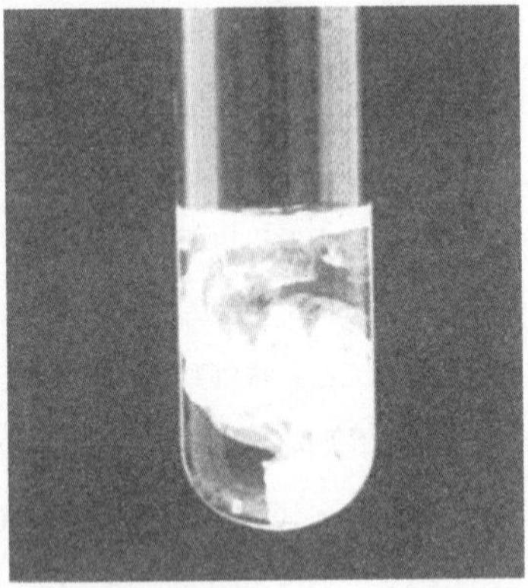

Addition of a solution of sodium chloride to a solution of silver nitrate yields a white precipitate of solid silver chloride.

If all strong bases and acids and most salts are completely ionized, it follows that molecular equations given above are not strictly appropriate when no molecules are actually present. Chemists differ somewhat in their views on writing such equations. Some argue that since it is simpler to write molecular equations, there is no harm in writing such equations in the molecular form as long as the chemist is fully aware of the ionic character of the reacting substances. Others insist on expressing highly ionized compounds only in the form of ionic symbols which is obviously more exact. It is of course essential to know the ionic or non-ionic nature of the compounds in advance.

A few simple rules needed for writing ionic equations are given below :

(*i*) All *strong electrolytes* are expressed in ionic symbols if they are soluble in water and all *weak electrolytes* and *covalent substances* are expressed in the molecular form.

(*ii*) Any electrolyte which is highly insoluble in water is generally written in the molecular form to indicate its insolubility. Actually, this is incorrect since many such solids are ionic in crystal form as well. This is, however, traditional.

(*iii*) In addition to the atoms which must balance on both sides of the equation, the ionic charges must also balance.

The following examples will illustrate the method of writing ionic equations for the given molecular equations:

(1) *Potassium chloride and silver nitrate react to produce potassium nitrate (soluble) and silver chloride (insoluble).*

Molecular : $KCl + AgNO_3 \rightarrow AgCl\downarrow + KNO_3$

Ionic : $K^+ + Cl^- + Ag^+ + NO_3^- \rightarrow AgCl\downarrow + K^+ + NO_3^-$

Since K^+ ions NO_3^- appear equally on both sides of the equation these may be cancelled and the ionic equation may simply be expressed as :

$$Ag^+ + Cl^- \rightarrow AgCl\downarrow$$

This ionic equation expresses all that actually happens.

(2) *Potassium sulphate and barium chloride solutions react to produce barium sulphate (insoluble) and potassium chloride (soluble).*

Molecular : $K_2SO_4 + BaCl_2 \rightarrow BaSO_4\downarrow + 2KCl$

Ionic : $2K^+ + SO_4^{2-} + Ba^{2+} + 2Cl^- \rightarrow BaSO_4\downarrow + 2K^+ + Cl^-$

Cancelling the ions common to both sides :

$$SO_4^{2-} + Ba^{2+} \rightarrow BaSO_4\downarrow$$

(3) *Sodium hydroxide and hydrochloric acid solutions react to produce sodium chloride (soluble) and water.*

Molecular : $NaOH + HCl \rightarrow NaCl + H_2O$

Ionic : $Na^+ + OH^- + H^+ + Cl^- \rightarrow Na^+ + Cl^- + H_2O$

Cancelling the ions common to both sides :

$$OH^- + H^+ \rightarrow H_2O$$

2. The Ion-Electron Method of Balancing Equations for Oxidation-Reduction or Redox Reactions. (By Use of Half-reactions). In this method the reaction is split up into two half-reactions. In one half-reaction the oxidizing agent picks up electrons and gets reduced, and in the other reducing agent is oxidized by supplying electrons. The two half-reactions are balanced separately and added in such a way that the electrons on the left of one and on the right of the other cancel out.

This procedure seems to imply that electrons are produced in redox reaction and travel through the solution from the reducing agent to the other species which is reduced. This is not true. We should, therefore, view the two half-reactions merely as a device for obtaining the final answer rather than as a mechanism of the reaction.

Different steps involved in writing a chemical equation by the ion-electron method are:

(1) Separate the oxidizing and the reducing agents.

(2) Write down one half-equation for the oxidizing agent changing into its reduced form.

(3) Write down the other half-equation showing the reducing agent changing into its oxidized form.

(4) Balance the atoms other than H an O for each half-reaction by adjusting coefficients, if necessary.

(5) Balance the oxygen atoms on the two sides by adding H_2O to the side deficient in oxygen.

(6) Balance the hydrogen atoms on the two sides by adding H^+ to the side deficient in hydrogen.

(7) Equalize the charge on both sides by adding electrons (e^-) to the side deficient in negative charge.

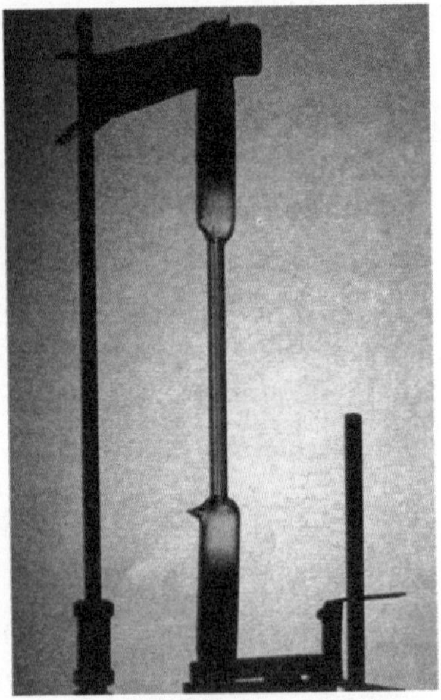

A hydrogen discharge tube showing the colour emitted by hydrogen atoms.

(8) If the reaction proceeds in basic solution, add enough OH^- on both sides of the half-reaction to get rid of H^+ appearing there. Combine H^+ and OH^- to give H_2O and remove H_2O duplication.

(9) Add these two balanced half-reactions in such a way that the electrons appearing on the right of one half-reaction and on the left of the other cancel. For this each half-reaction will be multiplied by some appropriate number before addition.

The following examples will illustrate the method.

Example 1. Write balanced equation for the oxidation of ferrous to ferric ion by dichromate ion in acid solution. The dichromate ion under these conditions yields Cr^{3+}

For one Half-Reaction

(*i*) Writing down the reactant and product of the half-reaction for the oxidizing agent changing into its reduced form :

$$Cr_2O_7^{2-} \rightarrow Cr^{3+}$$

(*ii*) Balancing the atoms other than oxygen :

$$Cr_2O_7^{2-} \rightarrow 2Cr^{3+}$$

(*iii*) Balancing oxygen atoms by adding $7H_2O$ on the right:

$$Cr_2O_7^{2-} \rightarrow 2Cr^{3+} + 7H_2O$$

(*iv*) Balancing hydrogen atoms by adding $14H^+$ on the left:

$$Cr_2O_7^{2-} + 14H^+ \rightarrow 2Cr^{3+} + 7H_2O$$

(*v*) Equalizing the charge by adding 6 electrons on the left :

$$Cr_2O_7^{2-} + 14H^+ + 6e^- \rightarrow 2Cr^{3+} + 7H_2O \quad \text{... (1)}$$

For the other Half-Reaction

(*i*) Writing down the reactant and product of the half-reaction for the reducing agent changing into its oxidized form :

$$Fe^{2+} \rightarrow Fe^{3+}$$

(*ii*) Equalizing the charge by adding one electron on the right :

$$Fe^{2+} \rightarrow Fe^{3+} + e \quad \text{....(2)}$$

Adding two Half-Reactions

Multiplying the half-reaction (2) by 6 and adding to the half-reaction (1)

$$Cr_2O_7^{2-} + 14H^+ + 6e^- \rightarrow 2Cr^{3+} + 7H_2O$$

$$6Fe^{2+} \rightarrow 6Fe^{3+} + 6e^-$$

$$Cr_2O_7^{2-} + 6Fe^{2+} + 14H^+ \rightarrow 2Cr^{3+} + 6Fe^{3+} + 7H_2O$$

Example 2. Balance the equation

$$H^+ + MnO_4^- + Fe^{2+} \rightarrow Fe^{3+} + Mn^{2+}$$

(*i*) Writing down the reactant and product of the half-reaction for the oxidizing agent changing into its reduced form :

$$MnO_4^- \rightarrow Mn^{2+}$$

(*ii*) Balancing the oxygen atoms by adding $4H_2O$ on the right :

$$MnO_4^- \rightarrow Mn^{2+} + 4H_2O$$

(*iii*) Balancing hydrogen atoms by adding $8H^+$ on the left :

$$MnO_4^- + 8H^+ \rightarrow Mn^{2+} + 4H_2O$$

(*iv*) Equalizing charge by adding 5 electrons on the left :

$$MnO_4^- + 8H^+ + 5e^- \rightarrow Mn^{2+} + 4H_2O \quad ...(1)$$

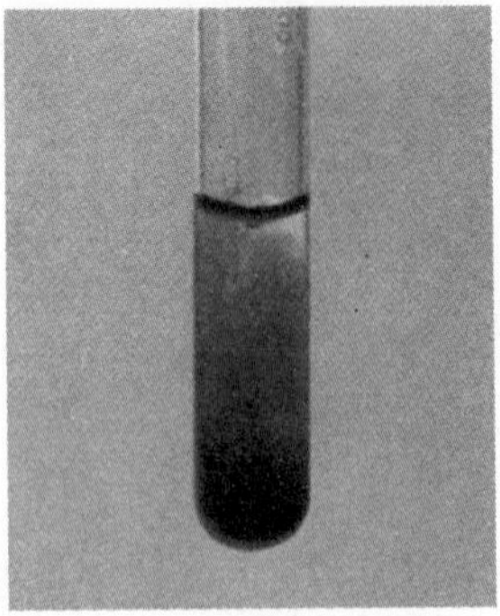

The confirmatory test for maganese (MNO_4^-)

Writing in a similar manner the half-reaction for the reducing agent changing into an oxidized form :

$$Fe^{2+} \rightarrow Fe^{3+} + e^- \quad ...(2)$$

Multiplying half-reaction (2) by 5 and adding up to (1), we obtain :

$$MnO_4^- + 8H^+ + 5Fe^{2+} \rightarrow Mn^{2+} + 5Fe^{3+} + 4H_2O$$

Example 3. Balance the equation

$$H_2C_2O_4 + H_2O_2 \rightarrow CO_2 + H_2O$$

(*a*) In this reaction oxalic acid is being oxidized to CO_2 and H_2O_2 is being reduced to H_2O.

(*b*) (*i*) Writing half-reaction for the oxidation of oxalic acid :

$$H_2C_2O_4 \rightarrow CO_2$$

(*ii*) Balancing the atoms in the order carbon—oxygen—hydrogen :

$$H_2C_2O_4 \rightarrow CO_2 + 2H^+$$

(*iii*) Equalizing the charge :

$$H_2C_2O_4 \rightarrow CO_2 + 2H^+ + 2e^- \quad ...(1)$$

(*c*) (*i*) Next writing the half-reaction for the reduction of H_2O_2

$$H_2O_2 \rightarrow H_2O$$

(*ii*) Balancing the atoms in the order oxygen –hydrogen :

$$H_2O_2 + 2H^+ \rightarrow 2H_2O$$

(*iii*) Equalizing the charge :

$$H_2O_2 + 2H^+ + 2e^- \rightarrow 2H_2O \qquad ...(2)$$

(*d*) Adding up (1) and (2) :

$$H_2C_2O_4 \rightarrow H_2O_2 + 2CO_2 + 2H_2O$$

Half-reactions of some important oxidizing and reducing agents used in volumetric analysis are given below for ready reference :

Oxidizing agents :

(*i*) *Potassium permanganate* (*acidic*).

$$MnO_4^- + 8H^+ + 5e^- \rightarrow Mn^{2+} + 4H_2O$$

(*ii*) *Potassium permanganate* (*alkaline*).

$$MnO_4^- + 2H_2O + 3e^- \rightarrow MnO_2 + 4OH^-$$

(*iii*) *Potassium dichromate* (*acidified*)

$$Cr_2O_7{}^{2-} + 14H^+ + 6e^- \rightarrow 2Cr^{3+} + 7H_2O$$

$K_2Cr_2\ O_7$ is orange in acidic solution. $Cr_2(SO_4)_3$ is green in acidic solution.

(*iv*) *Iodine.* $I_2 + 2e^- \rightarrow 2I^-$

(*v*) *Ferric chloride.*

$$Fe^{3+} + e^- \rightarrow Fe^{2+}$$

(*vi*) *Hydrogen peroxide.*

$$H_2O_2 + 2H^+ 2e^- \rightarrow 2H_2O$$

(*vii*) *Sodium hypochlorite*

$$ClO^- + H_2O + 2e^- \rightarrow Cl^- + 2OH^-$$

(*viii*) *Potassium iodate.*

$$IO_3^- + 6H^+ + 6e^- \rightarrow I^- + 3H_2O$$

(*ix*) *Chlorine.*

$$Cl_2 + 2e^- \rightarrow 2Cl^-$$

(*x*) *Bromine.*

$$Br_2 + 2e^- \rightarrow 2Br^-$$

(*xi*) *Mercuric salts* (two stages of reduction—to mercurous salts and to mercury).

$$2Hg^{2+} + 2e^- \rightarrow Hg_2{}^{2-}$$
$$Hg_2{}^{2+} + 2e^- \rightarrow 2Hg$$

(*xii*) *Hydrogen ions.*

$$2H^+ + 2e^- \rightarrow H_2$$

Bromine is a dark red liquid.

(*xiii*) *Manganese dioxide (acidified).*

$$MnO_2 + 4H^+ + 2e^- \rightarrow Mn^{2+} + 2H_2O$$

(*xiv*) *Nitric acid.* It can be reduced to various stages given below :

$$NO_3^- + 4H^+ + 3e^- \rightarrow NO + 2H_2O$$
$$NO_3^- + 2H^+ + e^- \rightarrow NO_2 + H_2O$$
$$2NO_3^- + 10H^+ + 8e^- \rightarrow N_2O + 5H_2O$$
$$NO_3^- + 10H^+ + 8e^- \rightarrow NH_4^+ + 3H_2O$$

Reducing Agents :

(*i*) *Oxalic acid.* $C_2O_4^{2-} \rightarrow 2CO_2 + 2e^-$

(*ii*) *Ferrous sulphate.* $Fe^{2+} \rightarrow Fe^{3+} + e^-$

(*iii*) *Sodium thiosulphate.* $2S_2O_3^{2-} \rightarrow S_4O_6^{2-} + 2e^-$

(*iv*) *Hydrogen peroxide* $H_2O_2 \rightarrow 2H^+ + O_2 + 2e^-$

(*v*) *Stannous chloride.* $Sn^{2+} \rightarrow Sn^{4+} + 2e^-$

(*vi*) *Hydrogen sulphide.* $H_2S \rightarrow 2H^+ + S^{2-}$

$$S^{2-} \rightarrow S + 2e^-$$

(vii) *Sulphurous acid.* $SO_3^{2-} + H_2O \rightarrow SO_4^{2-} + 2H^+ + 2e^-$

(viii) *Hydriodic acid.* (Acidified potassium iodide solution).

$$2I^- \rightarrow I_2 + 2e^-$$

TEST YOUR UNDERSTANDING

1. Fill in the blanks in the following :

(i) $NaCl + AgNO_3 \longrightarrow AgCl + NaNO_3$ is termed a / an .... equation.

(ii) $Cl^- + Ag^+ \longrightarrow AgCl$ is termed a /an..........equation.

(iii) All .... electrolytes are expressed in ionic symbols if they are .... in water.

(iv) All....... electrolytes and .... substances are expressed in molecular form.

(v) An electrolyte which is highly insoluble in water is written in........... to indicate its............

(vi) In an ionic equation both .... and ....must balance.

(vii) For balancing a redox reaction equation by ion-electron method, the reaction is split up into two............

(viii) In one ....the oxidizing agent............. electrons and gets............

(ix) In the other ....the reducing agent......... electrons and gets...........

(x) The two........... are balanced separately and added in such a way that the........ on the left of one and on the right of other.............

2. Complete the different steps involved in writing a chemical equation by the ion-electron method given below by inserting suitable words in the blanks.

(i) Separate the ....and the ....agents.

(ii) Write down one half-equation for the ....changing into its reduced form.

(iii) Write down the other half-equation for the changing into its oxidised form.

(iv) Balance the atoms other than ....and ....for each half-reaction by adjusting ...., if necessary.

(v) Balance the oxygen atoms on the two sides by adding ....to the side .... in oxygen.

(vi) Balance hydrogen atoms on the two sides by adding ....to the side ....in hydrogen.

(vii) Equalize the charge on both sides by adding......... to the side deficient in...........charge.

(viii) If the reaction proceeds in basic solution, add enough .... on both sides of the half reaction to get rid of ....appearing there. Combine ....and ....to give ....and remove .... duplication.

(*ix*) Add these two balanced half-reactions in such a way that the ....appearing on the right of one half-reaction and on the left of the other ....For this each half-reaction will be multiplied by some ....before adding.

KEY

1. (*i*) molecular ; (*ii*) ionic ; (*iii*) strong, soluble ; (*iv*) weak, covalent ; (*v*) molecular form, insolubility ; (*vi*) atoms, ionic charges ; (*vii*) half-reactions, (*viii*) half reaction; picks up, reduced ; (*ix*) half-reaction, supplies, oxidised ; (*x*) half-reactions, electrons, cancel.

2. (*i*) oxidising, reducing ; (*ii*) oxidising agent; (*iii*) reducing agent ; (*iv*) H, O, coefficients ; (*v*) H_2O, deficient ; (*vi*) H^+, deficient ; (*vii*) electrons, negative ; (*viii*) OH^-, H^+, H^+, OH^-, H_2O, H_2O , ; (*ix*) electrons, cancel, appropriate number.

EXERCISES

1. Balance the following equations by hit and trial method and rewrite them in the ionic form :

(*a*) $H_2SO_4 + NaOH \rightarrow Na_2SO_4 + H_2O$

(*b*) $Ba(OH)_2 + HBr \rightarrow BaBr_2 + H_2O$

(*c*) $BaCl_2 + Al_2(SO_4)_3 \rightarrow AlCl_3 + BaSO_4 \downarrow$

(*d*) $CuCl_2 + H_2S$ (weak acid) $\rightarrow HCl + CuS \downarrow$

(*e*) $Pb(NO_3)_2 + Fe_2(SO_4)_3 \rightarrow Fe(NO_3)_3 + PbSO_4 \downarrow$

(*f*) $CaCl_2 + K_3PO_4 \rightarrow KCl + Ca_3(PO_4)_2 \downarrow$

(*g*) $NH_4Cl + NaOH \rightarrow NaCl + NH_4OH$ (weak base)

(*h*) $KCN + H_2SO_4$ (Dilute) $\rightarrow K_2SO_4 + HCN$ (weak acid)

2. Complete and /or balance the following equations by the ion-electron method:

(1) $Br_2 + CO_3^{2-} \rightarrow Br^- + BrO_3^- + HCO_3^-$

(2) $MnO_2 + Cl^- \rightarrow Mn^{2+} + Cl_2$ in acid solution

(3) $Cu + NO_3^- \rightarrow Cu^{2+} + NO$ in acid solution

(4) $Cr_2O_7^{2-} + C_2O_4^{2-} \rightarrow Cr^{3+} + CO_2$ in acid solution

(5) $MnO_2 + C_2O_4^{2-} \rightarrow Mn^{2+} + CO_2$ in acidic solution

(6) $MnO_4^- + SO_3^{2-} \rightarrow MnO_4^{2-} + SO_4^{2-}$

(7) $S_2O_3^{2-} + I_2 \rightarrow S_4O_6^{2-} + I^-$ in basic solution.

(8) $Cr_2O_7^{2-} + Fe^{2+} + C_2O_4^{2-} \rightarrow Cr^{3+} + Fe^{3+} + CO_2$ in acid solution

(9) $P_4 \rightarrow H_2PO_2^- + PH_3$ in basic solution

(10) $MnO_4^{2-} \rightarrow MnO_4 + MnO_2$ in acid solution

(11) $I_2 + NO_3^- \rightarrow NO_2 + IO_3^-$ in acid solution.

3. Balance the following equations by the ion-electron method :

(1) $Na_2S_2O_3 + I_2 \rightarrow Na_2S_4O_6 + NaI$

(2) $H_3AsO_4 + KI + HCl \rightarrow H_3AsO_3 + KCl + I_2 + H_2O$

(3) $K_2Cr_2O_7 + KI + HCl \rightarrow I_2 + CrCl_3 + H_2O + KCl$

(4) $SbCl_5 + KI \rightarrow SbCl_3 + I_2 + KCl$

(5) $FeCl_3 + SnCl_2 \rightarrow SnCl_4 + FeCl_2$

(6) $CaC_2O_4 + H_2SO_4 + KMnO_4 \rightarrow CaSO_4 + K_2SO_4 + MnSO_4 + CO_2 + H_2O$

(7) $H_2SO_3 + I_2 + H_2O \rightarrow H_2SO_4 + HI$

(8) $KNO_2 + KMnO_4 + H_2SO_4 \rightarrow KNO_3 + K_2SO_4 + MnSO_4 + H_2O$

(9) $KMnO_4 + SbCl_3 + HCl \rightarrow KCl + MnCl_2 + SbCl_5 + H_2O$

(10) $NaClO_3 + KI + HCl \rightarrow NaCl + I_2 + KCl + H_2O$

(11) $Ce(SO_4)_2 + H_2C_2O_4 \rightarrow Ce_2(SO_4)_3 + H_2SO_4 + CO_2$

(12) $As + HNO_3 + H_2O \rightarrow H_3AsO_4 + NO$

(13) $Ag + HNO_3 + HNO_3 \rightarrow AgNO_3 + NO + H_2O$

(14) $CuS + HNO_3 + HNO_3 \rightarrow Cu(NO_3)_2 + S + NO + H_2$

(15) $H_2C_2O_4 + KMnO_4 + H_2SO_4 \rightarrow MnSO_4 + CO_2 + K_2SO_4$

(16) $Sn + HNO_3 \rightarrow SnO_2 + NO + H_2O$

(17) $PbCrO_4 + H_2SO_4 + FeSO_4 \rightarrow Fe_2(SO_4)_3 + PbSO_4 + Cr_2(SO_4)_3 + H_2O$

(18) $SbCl_3 + KIO_3 + HCl \rightarrow SbCl_5 + KI + H_2O$

(19) $Fe_2(SO_4)_3 + H_2SO_3 + H_2O \rightarrow FeSO_4 + H_2SO_4 + H_2SO_4$

(20) $SnCl_2 + HgCl_2 \rightarrow SnCl_4 + Hg_2Cl_2$

4. Balance the following equations by the ion-electron method :

(1) $MnO_4^- + Br^- \rightarrow Br_2 + MnO_2$ (acid solution)

(2) $Ag_2O + CH_2O \rightarrow Ag + HCO_2$ (basic solution)

(3) $H_2SO_3 + Fe^{3+} \rightarrow Fe^{2+} + SO_4^{2-}$ (acid solution)

(4) $Sn^{2+} + Cr_2O_7^{2+} \rightarrow Sn^{4+} + Cr^{3+}$ (acid solution)

(5) $MnO_4^- + Sn^{2+} \rightarrow Mn^{2+} + Sn^{4+}$ (acid solution)

(6) $CrO_4^- + HSnO_2^- \rightarrow CrO_2^- + HSnO_3^-$ (basic solution)

(7) $BaO_2 + Cl^- \rightarrow Ba^{2+} + Cl_2$ (acid solution)

(8) $C_2H_4O + NO_3^- \rightarrow C_2H_4O_2 + NO$ (acid solution)

(9) $CrO_2^- + ClO^- \rightarrow Cl^- + CrO_4^{2-}$ (basic solution)

(10) $H_3AsO_4 + I \rightarrow H_3AsO_3 + I_2$ (acid solution)

(11) $Mn^{2+} + Br_2 \rightarrow MnO_2 + Br^-$ (basic solution)

(12) $Cr(OH)_4^- + H_2O_2 \rightarrow CrO_4^{2-}$ (basic solution)

(13) $PbO_2 + Cl^- \rightarrow Pb^{2+} + Cl_2$ (acid solution)

(14) $MnO_4^- + H_2S \rightarrow Mn^{2+} + S$ (acid solution)

(15) $Cr_2O_7^{2-} + HNO_2 \rightarrow Cr^{3+} + NO_3^-$ (acid solution)

(16) $MnO_4^- + NO_2^- \rightarrow MnO_2 + NO_3^-$ (basic solution)

(17) $H_2C_2O_4 + MnO_2 \rightarrow Mn^{2+} + CO_2$ (acid solution)

(18) $MnO_4^- + C_2H_4 \rightarrow Mn^{2+} + CO_2$ (acid solution)

(19) $Br_2 \rightarrow BrO_3^- + Br^-$ (basic solution)

(20) $H_2S + I_2 \rightarrow S + I^-$ (acid solution)

ANSWERS

1. (*a*) $H_2SO_4 + 2NaOH \rightarrow Na_2SO_4 + 2H_2O$

$H^+ + OH^- \rightarrow H_2O$

(*b*) $Ba(OH)_2 + 2HBr \rightarrow BaBr_2 + 2H_2O$

$H^+ + OH^- \rightarrow H_2O$

(*c*) $3BaCl_2 + Al_2(SO_4)_3 \rightarrow 2AlCl_3 + 3BaSO_4$

$Ba^{2+} + SO_4^{2-} \rightarrow BaSO_4$

(*d*) $CuCl_2 + H_2S \rightarrow 2HCl + CuS$

$Cu^{2+} + H_2S \rightarrow CuS + 2H^+$

(*e*) $3Pb(NO_3)_2 + Fe_2(SO_4)_3 \rightarrow 2Fe(NO_3)_3 + 3\ PbSO_4$

$Pb^{2+} + SO_4^{2-} \rightarrow PbSO_4$

(*f*) $3CaCl_2 + 2K_3PO_4 \rightarrow 6KCl + Ca_3(PO_4)_2$

$3Ca^{2+} + 2PO_4^{3-} \rightarrow Ca_3(PO_4)_2$

(*g*) $NH_4Cl + NaOH \rightarrow NaCl + NH_4OH$

$NH_4^+ + OH^- \rightarrow NH_4OH$

(*h*) $2KCN + H_2SO_4 \rightarrow K_2SO_4 + 2HCN$

$CN^- + H^+ \rightarrow HCN$

2. (1) $Br_2 + 2e^- \rightarrow 2Br^-] \times 5$

$Br_2 + 6H_2O \rightarrow 2BrO_3^- + 12H^+ + 10e^-$

$CO_3^{2-} + H^+ \rightarrow HCO_3^-] \times 12$

$6Br_2 + 6H_2O + 12CO_3^{2-} \rightarrow 10Br^- + 2BrO_3^- + 12HCO_3^-$

or $3Br_2 + 3H_2O + 6CO_3^{2-} \rightarrow 5Br^- + BrO_3^- + BrO_3^- + 6HCO_3^-$

(2) $MnO_2 + 4H^+ + 2e^- \rightarrow Mn^{2+} + H_2O$

$2Cl^- \rightarrow Cl_2 + 2e^-$

$MnO_2 + 4H^+ + 2Cl^- \rightarrow Mn^{2+} + Cl_2 + 2H_2O$

(3) $Cu \rightarrow Cu^{2+} + 2e^{-}] \times 3$

$NO_3^{-} + 4H^{+} + 3e^{-} \rightarrow NO + 2H_2O] \times 2$

$$3Cu + 2NO_3^{-} + 8H^{+} \rightarrow 3Cu^{2+} + 2NO + 4H_2O$$

(4) $Cr_2O_7^{2-} + 14H^{+} + 6e^{-} \rightarrow 2Cr^{3+} + 7H_2O$

$C_2O_4^{2-} \rightarrow 2CO_2 + +2e] \times 3$

$$Cr_2O_7^{2-} + 14H^{+} + 3C_2O_4^{2-} \rightarrow 2Cr^{3+} + 6CO_2 + 7H_2O$$

(5) $MnO_2 + 4H^{+} + 2e^{-} \rightarrow Mn^{2+} + 2H_2O$

$C_2O_4^{2-} \rightarrow 2CO_2 + 2e^{-}$

$$MnO_2 + 4H^{+} + C_2O_4^{2-} \rightarrow Mn^{2+} + 2H_2O + 2CO_2$$

(6) $MnO_4^{-} + e^{-} \rightarrow MnO_4^{2-}] \times 2$

$SO_3^{2-} + H_2O \rightarrow SO_4^{2-} + 2H^{+} + 2e$

$$2MnO_4^{-} + SO_3^{2-} + H_2O \rightarrow 2MnO_4^{2-} + 2H^{+} + SO_4^{2-}$$

(7) $2S_2O_3^{2-} \rightarrow S_4O_6^{2-} + 2e^{-}$ $\quad I_2 + 2e^{-} \rightarrow 2I^{-}$

$$2S_2O_3^{2-} + I_2 \rightarrow S_4O_6^{2-} + 2I^{-}$$

(8) $Cr_2O_7^{2-} + 14H^{+} + 6e^{-} \rightarrow 2Cr^{3+} + 7H_2O$

$Fe^{2+} + C_2O_4^{2-} \rightarrow Fe^{3+} + 2CO_2 + 3e^{-}] \times 2$

$$Cr_2O_7^{2-} + 14H^{+} + 2Fe^{2+} + 2C_2SO_4^{2-}$$
$$\rightarrow 2Cr^{3+} + 2Fe^{3+} + 4CO_2 + 7H_2O$$

(9) $P + 2OH^{-} \rightarrow H_2PO_2^{-} + e^{-}] \times 3$

$P + 3H_2O + 3e^{-} \rightarrow PH_3 + 3OH^{-}$

$$4P + 3OH^{-} + 3H_2O \rightarrow 3H_2PO_2^{-} + PH_3$$

(10) $MnO_4^{2-} \rightarrow MnO_4^{-} + e^{-}] \times 2$

$MnO_4^{2-} + 4H^{+} + 2e^{-} \rightarrow MnO_2 + 2H_2O$

$$3MnO_4^{2-} + 4H^{+} \rightarrow 2MnO_4^{-} + MnO_2 + 2H_2O$$

(11) $I_2 + 6H_2O \rightarrow 2IO_3^- + 12H^+ + 10e^-$

$NO_3^- + 2H^+ + e^- \rightarrow NO_2 + H_2O] \times 10$

$I_2 + 10NO_3^- + 8H^+ \rightarrow 2IO_3^- + 10NO_2 + 4H_2O$

3. (1) $2S_2O_3^{2-} \rightarrow S_4O_6^{2-} + 2e^-$

$I_2 + 2e^- \rightarrow 2I^-$

$2S_2O_3^{2-} + I_2 \rightarrow S_4O_6^{2-} + 2I^-$

(2) $H_3AsO_4 + 2H^+ + 2e^- \rightarrow H_3AsO_3 + H_2O$

$2I^- \rightarrow I_2 + 2e^-$

$H_3AsO_4 + 2I^- + 2H^+ \rightarrow H_3AsO_3 + H_2O + I_2$

(3) $Cr_2O_7^{2-} + 14H^+ + 6e^- \rightarrow 2Cr^{3+} + 7H_2O$

$2I^- \rightarrow I_2 + 2e^-] \times 3$

$Cr_2O_7^{2-} + 6I^- + 14H^+ \rightarrow 2Cr^{3+} + 3I_2 + 7H_2O$

(4) $SbCl_5 + 2e^- \rightarrow SbCl_3 + 2Cl^-$

$2I^- \rightarrow I_2 + 2e^-$

$SbCl_5 + 2I^- \rightarrow SbCl_3 + 2Cl^- + I_2$

(5) $Fe^{3+} + e^- \rightarrow Fe^{2+}] \times 2$

$SnCl_2 + 2Cl^- \rightarrow SnCl_4 + 2e^-$

$2Fe^{3+} + SnCl_2 + 2Cl^- \rightarrow SnCl_4 + 2Fe^{2+}$

(6) $C_2O_4^{2-} \rightarrow 2CO_2 + 2e] \times 5$

$MnO_4^{2-} + 8H^+ + 5e^- \rightarrow Mn^{2+} + 4H_2O] \times 2$

$5C_2O_4^{2-} + MnO_4^- + 16H^+ \rightarrow 10CO_2 + 2Mn^{2+} + 8H_2O$

(7) $H_2SO_3 + H_2O \rightarrow SO_4^{2-} + 4H^+ + 2e^-$

$I_2 + 2e^- \rightarrow 2I^-$

$H_2SO_3 + I_2 + H_2O \rightarrow SO_4^{2-} + 4H^+ + 2I^-$

(8) $NO_2^- + H_2O \rightarrow NO_3^- + 2H^+ + 2e^-]\times 5$

$MnO_4^- + 8H^+ + 5e^- \rightarrow Mn^{2+} + 4H_2O]\times 2$

$5NO_2^2 + 2MnO_4^- + 6H^+ \rightarrow 5NO_3^- + 2Mn^{2+} + 3H_2O$

(9) $SbCl_3 + 2Cl^- \rightarrow SbCl_5 + 2e^-]\times 5$

$MnO_4^- + 8H^+ + 5e^- \rightarrow Mn^{2+} + 4H_2O]\times 2$

$5SbCl_3 + 10Cl^- + 2MnO_4^- + 16H^+ \rightarrow 5SbCl_5 + 2Mn^{2+} + 8H_2O$

(10) $ClO_3^- + 6H^+ + 6e^- \rightarrow Cl^- + 3H_2O$

$2I^- \rightarrow I_2 + 2e^-]\times 3$

$ClO_3^- + 6I^- + 6H^+ \rightarrow Cl^- + 3I_2 + 3H_2O$

(11) $Ce^{4+} + e^- \rightarrow Ce^{3+}]\times 2$

$C_2O_4^{2-} \rightarrow 2CO_2 + 2e^-$

$2Ce^{4+} + C_2O_4^{2-} \rightarrow 2Ce^{3+} + 2CO_2$

(12) $As + 4H_2O \rightarrow H_3AsO_4 + 5H^+ + 5e^-]\times 3$

$NO_3^- + 4H^+ + 3e^- \rightarrow NO + 2H_2O]\times 5$

$3As + 5NO_3^- + 5H^+ + 2H_2O \rightarrow 3H_3AsO_4 + 5NO$

(13) $Ag \rightarrow Ag^+ + e^-]\times 3$

$NO_3^- + 4H^+ + 3e^- \rightarrow NO + 2H_2O$

$3Ag + NO_3^- + 4H^+ \rightarrow 3Ag^+ + NO + 2H_2O$

(14) $S^{2-} \rightarrow S + 2e^-]\times 3$

$NO_3^- + 4H^+ + 3e^- \rightarrow NO + 2H_2O]\times 2$

$3S^{2-} + 2NO_3^- + 8H^+ \rightarrow 3S + 2NO + 4H_2O$

(15) $C_2O_4^{2-} \rightarrow 2CO_2 + 2e^-]\times 5$

$MnO_4^- + 8H^+ + 5e^- \rightarrow Mn^{2+} + 4H_2O]\times 2$

$5C_2O_4^{2-} + 2MnO_4^- + 16H^+ \rightarrow 10CO_2 + 2Mn^{2+} + 8H_2O$

(16) $Sn + 2H_2O \rightarrow SnO_2 + 4H^+ + 4e^-]\times 3$

$NO_3^- + 4H^+ + 3e^- \rightarrow NO + 2H_2O]\times 4$

$3Sn + 4NO_3^- + 4H^+ \rightarrow 3SnO_2 + 4NO + 2H_2O$

(17) $CrO_4^{2-} + 8H^+ + 3e^- \rightarrow Cr^{3+} + 4H_2O$

$Fe^{2+} \rightarrow Fe^{3+} + e^-]\times 3$

$CrO_4^{2-} + 3Fe^{2+} + 8H^+ \rightarrow Cr^{3+} + 3Fe^{3+} + 4H_2O$

(18) $SbCl_3 + 2Cl^- \rightarrow SbCl_5 + 2e^-]\times 3$

$IO_3^- + 6H^+ + 6e^- \rightarrow I^- + 3H_2O$

$3SbCl_3 + 6Cl^- + IO_3^- + 6H^+ \rightarrow 3SbCl_5 + I^- + 3H_2O$

(19) $Fe^{3+} + e^- \rightarrow Fe^{2+}]\times 2$

$H_2SO_3 + H_2O \rightarrow SO_4^{2-} + 4H^+ + 2e^-$

$2Fe^{3+} + H_2SO_3 + H_2O \rightarrow 2Fe^{2+} + SO_4^{2-} + 4H^+$

(20) $Sn^{2+} \rightarrow Sn^{4+} + 2e^-$

$2Hg^{2+} + 2e^- \rightarrow Hg_2^{2+}$

$Sn^{2+} + 2Hg^{2+} \rightarrow Sn^{4+} + Hg_2^{2+}$

4. (1) $MnO_4^- + 4H^+ + 3e^- \rightarrow MnO_2 + 2H_2O]\times 2$

$2Br^- \rightarrow Br_2 + 2e^-]\times 3$

$2MnO_4^- + 8H^+ + 6Br^- \rightarrow 2MnO_2 + H_2O + 3Br_2$

(2) $Ag_2O + 2H^+ + 2e^- \rightarrow 2Ag + H_2O$

$CH_2O + H_2O + OH^- \rightarrow HCO_2^2 + 3H^+ + 2e^- + OH^-$

$Ag_2O + CH_2O + OH^- \rightarrow 2Ag + HCO_2^- + H_2O$

(3) $H_2SO_3 + H_2O \rightarrow SO_4^{2-} + 4H^+ + 2e^-$

$Fe^{3+} + e^- \rightarrow Fe^{2+}]\times 2$

$H_2SO_3 + H_2O + 2Fe^{3+} \rightarrow SO_4^{2-} + 4H^+ + 2Fe^{2+}$

(4) $Cr_2O_7^{2-} + 14H^+ + 6e^- \rightarrow 2Cr^{3+} + 7H_2O$

$Sn^{2+} \rightarrow Sn^{4+} + 2e^-]\times 5$

$Cr_2O_7^{2-} + 3Sn^{2+} + 14H^+ \rightarrow 2Cr^{3+} + 3Sn^{4+} + 7H_2O$

(5) $MnO_4^{2-} + 8H^- + 5e^- \rightarrow Mn^{2+} + 4H_2O] \times 2$

$Sn^{2+} \rightarrow Sn^{4+} + 2e^-] \times 5$

$2MnO_4^- + 16H^+ + 5Sn^{2+} \rightarrow 2Mn^{2+} + 5Sn^{4+} + 8H_2O$

(6) $CrO_4^{2-} + 4H^+ + 4OH^- + 3e^- \rightarrow CrO_2^- + 2H_2O + 4OH^-] \times 2$

$HSnO_2^- + H_2O + 2OH^- \rightarrow HSnO_3^- + 2H^+ + 2OH^- + 2e^-] \times 3$

$2CrO_4^{2-} + 2HSnO_2^- + H_2O \rightarrow CrO_2^- + 3HSnO_3^- + 2OH^-$

(7) $BaO_2 + 4H^+ + 2e^- \rightarrow Ba^{2+} + 2H_2O$

$2Cl^- \rightarrow Cl_2 + 2e^-$

$BaO_2 + 4H^+ + 2Cl^- \rightarrow Ba^{2+} + 2H_2O + Cl_2$

(8) $C_2H_4O + H_2O \rightarrow C_2H_4O_2 + 2H^+ + 2e^-] \times 3$

$NO_3^- + 4H^+ + 3e^- \rightarrow NO + 2H_2O] \times 2$

$3C_2H_4O + 2NO_3^- + 2H^+ \rightarrow 3C_2H_4O_2 + 2NO + H_2O$

(9) $CrO_2^- + 2H_2O + 4OH^- \rightarrow CrO_4^{2-} + 4H^+ + 4OH^- + 3e^-] \times 2$

$ClO^- + 2H^+ + 2OH^- + 2e \rightarrow Cl^- + H_2O + 2OH^-] \times 3$

$2CrO_2^- + 3ClO^- + 2OH^- \rightarrow 2CrO_4^{2-} + 3Cl^- + H_2O$

(10) $H_3AsO_4 + 2H^+ + 2e^- \rightarrow H_3AsO_3 + H_2O$

$2I^- \rightarrow I_2 + 2e^-$

$H_3AsO_4 + 2I^- + 2H^+ \rightarrow H_3AsO_3 + H_2O + I_2$

(11) $Mn^{2+} + 2H_2O + 4OH^- \rightarrow MnO_2 + 4H^+ + 4OH^- + 2e^-$

$Br_2 + 2e^- \rightarrow 2Br^-$

$Mn^{2+} + Br_2 + 4OH^- \rightarrow MnO_2 + 2Br^- + 2H_2O$

(12) $Cr(OH)_4^- + 4OH^- \rightarrow CrO_4^{2-} + 4H^+ + 4OH^- + 3e^-] \times 2$

$H_2O_2 + 2H^+ + 2OH^- + 2e^- \rightarrow 2H_2O + 2OH^-] \times 3$

$2Cr(OH)_4^- + 3H_2O_2 + 2OH^- \rightarrow 2CrO_4^{2-} + 8H_2O$

(13) $PbO_2 + 4H^+ + 2e^- \rightarrow Pb^{2+} + 2H_2O$

$$2Cl^- \rightarrow Cl_2 + 2e^-$$

$$PbO_2 + 4H^+ + 2Cl^- \rightarrow Pb^{2+} + Cl_2 + 2H_2O$$

(14) $MnO_4^- + 8H^+ + 5e^- \rightarrow Mn^{2+} + 4H_2O] \times 2$

$$H_2S \rightarrow S + 2H^+ + 2e^-] \times 5$$

$$2MnO_4^- + 5H_2S + 6H^+ \rightarrow 2Mn^{2+} + 5S + 8H_2O$$

(15) $H^+ + 6e^- \rightarrow 2Cr^{3+} + 7H_2O$

$$HNO_2 + H_2O \rightarrow NO_3^- + 3H^+ + 2e^-] \times 3$$

$$Cr_2O_7^{2-} + 3HNO_2 + 5H^+ \rightarrow 2Cr^{3+} + 3NO_3^- + 4H_2O$$

(16) $MnO_4^- + 4H^+ + 4OH^- + 3e^- \rightarrow MnO_2 + 2H_2O + 4OH^-] \times 2$

$$NO_2^- + H_2O + 2OH^- \rightarrow NO_3^- + 2H^+ + 2OH^- + 2e^-] \times 3$$

$$2MnO_4^- + 3NO_2^- + H_2O \rightarrow 2MnO_2 + 3NO_3^- + 2OH^-$$

(17) $MnO_2 + 4H^+ + 2e^- \rightarrow Mn^{2+} + 2H_2O$

$$H_2C_2O_4 \rightarrow 2CO_2 + 2H^+ + 2e^-$$

$$MnO_2 + H_2C_2O_4 + 2H^+ \rightarrow Mn^{2+} + 2CO_2 + H_2O$$

(18) $MnO_4^- + 8H^+ + 5e^- \rightarrow Mn^{2+} + 4H_2O] \times 12$

$$C_2H_4 + 4H_2O \rightarrow 2CO_2 + 12H^+ + 12e^-] \times 5$$

$$12MnO_4^- + 5C_2H_4 + 36H^+ \rightarrow 12Mn^{2+} + 10CO_2 + 28H_2O$$

(19) $Br_2 + 6H_2O + 12OH^- \rightarrow 2BrO_3^- + 12H^+ + 12OH^- + 10e^-$

$$Br_2 + 2e^- \rightarrow 2Br^-] \times 5$$

$$6Br_2 + 12OH^- \rightarrow 2BrO_3^- + 10Br^- + 6H_2O$$

or $3Br_2 + 6OH^- \rightarrow BrO_3^- + 5Br^- + 3H_2O$

(20) $H_2S \rightarrow S + 2H^+ + 2e^-$

$$I_2 + 2e^- \rightarrow 2I^-$$

$$H_2S + I_2 \rightarrow S + 2H^+ + 2I^-$$

6 CHAPTER

Oxidation-Reduction Reactions

1. Oxidation Numbers. Oxidation is any reaction in which an atom or ion loses electrons. On the other hand, reduction is defined as any reaction in which an atom or ion gains electrons. As oxidation involves removal of electrons, it has also been termed *de-electronation.* Similarly reduction may be referred to as *electronation*.

Change of ferrous (Fe^{2+}) to ferric (Fe^{3+}), stannous (Sn^{2+}) to stannic (Sn^{4+}), manganate (MnO_4^{2-}) to permanganate (MnO_4^-) are all cases of oxidation as each one of them involves loss of electrons.

$$Fe^{2+} + \longrightarrow Fe^{3+} + 1\ \textit{electron}$$
$$Sn^{2+} + \longrightarrow Sn^{4+} + 2\ \textit{electrons}$$
$$MnO_4^{2-} \longrightarrow MnO_4^- + 1\ \textit{electron}$$

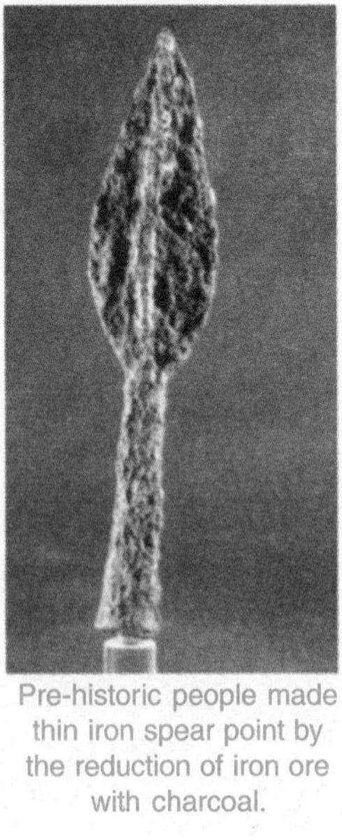

Pre-historic people made thin iron spear point by the reduction of iron ore with charcoal.

Similarly formation of mercurous ions (Hg_2^{2+}) from mercuric ions (Hg^{2+}) and formation of chloride ions (Cl^-) from chlorine atoms are cases of reduction as both involve a gain of electrons.

$2Hg^{2+}$	+	2 electrons	$\longrightarrow$	Hg_2^{2+}
Mercuric ions				Mercurous ion
Cl	+	1 electron	$\longrightarrow$	Cl^-
Chlroine atom				Chloride ion

In order to keep track of electron shifts in oxidation-reduction reactions, it is convenient to use the concept of oxidation number or oxidation state of various atoms involved in these reactions. *The oxidation number is defined as the formal charge which an atom appears to have when electrons are counted* in accordance with the following rather arbitrary rules :

(*a*) *Electrons shared between two unlike atoms are counted with more electronegative atom.* For example, the electron pair shared between H and Cl in $\overset{+1}{H}:\overset{-1}{\ddot{\underset{\cdot\cdot}{Cl}}}:$ is counted with more electronegative Cl. As a result of it hydrogen having lost share in the electron pair appears to have +1 charge and chlorine appears to have –1 charge. Hence oxidation numbers of H and Cl are +1 and –1 respectively.

Hydrogen has become a fuel in space exploration.

(*b*) *Electrons shared between two like atoms are divided equally between the two sharing atoms.* For example, in hydrogen molecule, H : H, the electron pair is equally shared between the two atoms. Thus both the atoms appear to have no charge *i.e.*, oxidation number of hydrogen is zero in hydrogen molecule.

In the molecule of water given in the margin, the two electron pairs shared between oxygen and the two hydrogen atoms are counted with the more electronegative atom. Hence in water, oxidation number of each H is +1 and that of the O atom is –2.

$$\overset{+1}{H}\ :\overset{-2}{\ddot{\underset{\cdot\cdot}{O}}}:\ \overset{+1}{H}$$

Water

Counting of electrons like this is very laborious. The following operational rules derived from the above will be found very convenient :

(1) In the elementary or uncombined state, the atoms are assigned an oxidation number zero.

(2) In compounds, the oxidation number of fluorine is always –1.

(3) In compounds, the group IA elements (Li, Na, K, Rb, Cs and Fr) have an oxidation number +1 and the group IIA elements. (Be, Mg, Ca, Sr, Ba and Ra) have an oxidation number +2.

(4) Oxidation number of hydrogen in compounds is generally +1 except in metalic hydrides wherein its oxidation number is –1.

(5) In compounds, the oxidation number of oxygen is generally –2 except in F_2O wherein oxidation number of fluorine is –1 and that of oxygen is + 2. In hydrogen peroxide molecule the electron pair shared between O and H is counted with O but the other electron pair shared between two O atoms is equally shared. The number of electrons counted with each O is, therefore, seven (*i.e.*, one more than its own electrons). The oxygen atom, therefore, appears to have –1 charge or its oxidation number in H_2O_2 is –1.

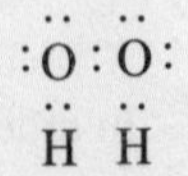

Hydrogen Peroxide

(6) In neutral molecules, the sum of the oxidation numbers of all the atoms is zero.

(7) For complex ions (charged species), the sum of the oxidation numbers of ali the atoms is equal to the net charge on the ion.

With the help of these operational rules we can calculate the oxidation number of an atom present in a molecule or complex ion as illustrated in the following examples :

Example 1. What is the oxidation number of S in (*a*) H_2SO_4, (*b*) $H_2S_2O_7$, (*c*) $Na_2S_2O_3$?

(*a*) Let the oxidation number of S be *x*.

Sum of oxidation numbers of various atoms in H_2SO_4

$$= 2 \times (+1) + x + 4 \times (-2)$$
$$= 2 + x - 8 = x - 6$$

This sum must be zero (rule 6). Hence

$$x - 6 = 0$$

whence $x = 6$

or Oxidation number of S in H_2SO_4 = + 6.

(*b*) Sum of oxidation numbers of various atoms in $H_2S_2O_7$

$$= 2 \times (+1) + 2x + 7 \times (-2)$$
$$= 2 + 2x - 14 = 2x - 12$$

Putting $2x - 12 = 0$ as above, we have

$$x = +6$$

Oxidation number of S in $H_2S_2O_7$ = + 6.

(*c*) Sum of oxidation numbers of various atoms in $Na_2S_2O_3$

$$= 2 \times (+1) + 2x + 3 \times (-2)$$
$$= 2 + 2x - 6 = 2x - 4$$

Putting $2x - 4 = 0$

$x = +2$

$\therefore$ Oxidation number of S in $Na_2S_2O_3 = +2$.

2. Covalency, Oxidation State and Oxidation Number. Covalency of an element is defined as a *number* indicating its combining capacity. For example, it represents the number of hydrogen atoms which can combine with a given atom. It also represents the number of single bonds which an atom can form. It is also defined as the number of electrons its atom is able to share. *In any case covalency is a pure number and has no plus or minus sign associated with it.*

The two teams are joined together because both are holding onto the same rope. In a similar way, two atoms are bonded together when both hold onto the same electrons.

Oxidation number is defined as the charge which an atom appears to have when electrons are counted. It is *positive* or *negative.* For example, in ammonia the covalency of nitrogen is three but its oxidation number is –3.

In ionic compounds the oxidation state of an element is the same as the charge on the ion formed from an atom of the element. For example, in potassium bromide potassium is said to be in the +1 oxidation state and bromine in –1 oxidation state. It ionizes as

$$KBr \rightleftharpoons K^+ + Br$$

In other words, oxidation numbers of potassium and bromide are +1 and –1 respectively.

Oxidation state of aluminium in Al_2O_3 is +3 and the total oxidation number of two aluminium atoms is +6. Thus *oxidation state of an element is its oxidation number per atom.*

There may actually be a difference between the magnitude of covalency and the oxidation number. For example, consider the following compounds of carbon :

CH_4	CH_3Cl	CH_2Cl_2
Methane	Methyl chloride	Methylene chloride
	$CHCl_3$	CCl_4
	Chloroform	Carbon tetrachloride

This care runs on CNG which is 90 per cent methane.

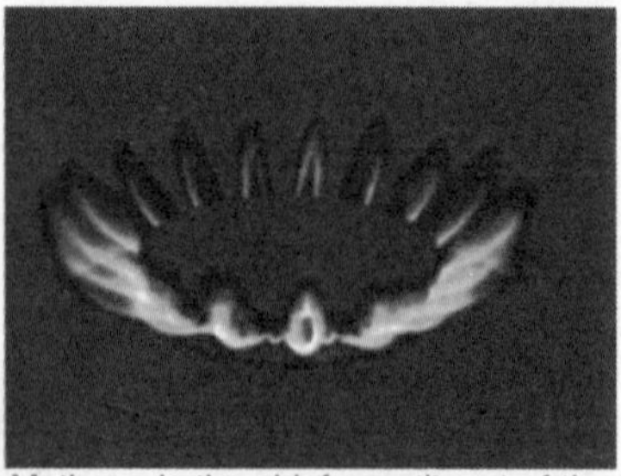

Methane is the chief constituent of the natural gas we use for heating and cooking.

In each case one atom of carbon shares a total of 4 pairs of electrons with other atoms. Carbon atom is, therefore, tetracovalent in each case.

Oxidation number for carbon in $CH_4, CH_3Cl, CH_2Cl_2, CHCl_3$ and CCl_4 $-4, -2, 0, +2$ and $+4$ respectively.

Thus, while covalency of carbon remains constant (= 4) in each one of the five compounds, its oxidation number varies from -4 to $+4$.

3. Oxidation and Reduction in Terms of Oxidation Numbers. The term **oxidation** *refers to any chemical change involving increase in oxidation number whereas the term* **reduction** *applies to any chemical change involving decrease in oxidation number.*

Consider the following chemical changes :

$$2H_2 + O_2 \longrightarrow 2H_2O$$

Herein oxidation number of hydrogen changes from zero (in H_2) to +1 [in H_2O]. It is, therefore, a case of oxidation of hydrogen.

The oxidation number of oxygen decreases from zero (in O_2) to –2 (in H_2O). It is, therefore, a case of reduction of oxygen.

In the same reaction, oxidation number of hydrogen increases and that of oxygen decreases, *i.e.*, hydrogen undergoes oxidation while oxygen undergoes reduction. Thus oxidation and reduction occur together.

4. Balancing of Chemical Equations by Oxidation Number Method. The principle underlying this universally applicable method of balancing equations is that electrical charge must be conserved in the course of chemical reaction, *i.e.*, any increase in oxidation number must be compensated by a decrease.

In brief, the method, therefore, consists in selection of such coefficients for the oxidizing and reducing agents as will ensure to make the total decrease in oxidation number for the former equal to the total increase in oxidation number for the latter.

The systematic procedure for the same involves the following steps :

(*i*) Assign oxidation numbers to the atoms that change.

(*ii*) Choose the proper ratio of oxidizing agent to the reducing agent so that the oxidation number change is balanced.

(*iii*) Make appropriate change in the coefficient of the products corresponding to the change in the coefficient of reactants in step (*ii*).

(*iv*) Balance the oxygen atoms on both sides by adding H_2O to the side that is deficient in oxygen.

(*v*) Balance the hydrogen atoms on both sides by adding H^+ to the side that is deficient in hydrogen.

(*vi*) The equation is balanced if the reaction is taking place in acidic solution. If, however, the reaction proceeds in basic solution, and sufficient number of OH^- to get rid of H^+ but add equal number of OH^- on both sides.

(*vii*) Cancel any duplication that might have crept in on both sides of the equation.

The following examples will illustrate the method:

Example 1. Oxidation of ammonia by copper oxide to give copper, nitrogen and water, is represented as under :

(*i*) Writing skeleton equation with oxidation number of copper and nitrogen,—

Oxidation number

Skeleton $\overset{+2}{CuO}_{\uparrow 2e^-} + \overset{-3}{NH_3}_{\downarrow 3e^-} \rightarrow \overset{0}{Cu} + \overset{0}{N_2} + H_2O$

An open-pit copper mine near Baghdad, Arizona.

(*ii*) Oxidation number of Cu changes from +2 to 0 and that of N changes from –3 to 0. The Cu atom in going from +2 to 0 has to gain two units of negative charge. We can show it by an arrow going upward to Cu and labelling it $2e^-$. The N atom in going from –3 to 0 has to get rid of 3 units of negative charge. We can indicate it by an arrow going down from nitrogen and labelling it $3e^-$.

(*iii*) To balance the oxidation number change multiply CuO by 3 and NH_3 by 2. Then provide same number of Cu and N atoms on the right. The equation now reads :

Incomplete : $3CuO + 2NH_3 \rightarrow 3Cu + N_2 + H_2O$

(*iv*) Balancing oxygen by multiplying H_2O by 3, we get the completed equation.

Balanced : $3CuO + 2NH_3 \rightarrow 3Cu + N_2 + 3H_2O$

In this the hydrogen atoms are already balanced.

Example 2. Write a complete balanced equation for the change

$$Cr_2O_7^{2-} + H_2SO_3 \rightarrow Cr^{3+} + HSO_4^-$$

taking place in acidic solution.

(*i*) Writing skeleton equation with oxidation numbers of chromium and sulphur –

$$\begin{array}{lccccccc} \text{oxidation numbers} & +6 & & +4 & & +3 & & +6 \\ \text{Skeleton} & Cr_2O_7^{2-} & + & H_2SO_3 & \rightarrow & Cr^{3+} & + & HSO_4^- \\ & \uparrow 2\times 3e^- & & \downarrow 2e^- & & & & \end{array}$$

(*ii*) Oxidation number of Cr changes from + 6 in $Cr_2O_7^{2-}$ to +3 in Cr^{3+}. This is a $3e^-$ gain. There being 2 Cr atoms in $Cr_2O_7^{2-}$ there is total of $6e^-$ gain.

Oxidation number of S changes from +4 in H_2SO_3 to +6 in HSO_4^-. This is a $2e^-$ loss.

(*iii*) To balance the oxidation number change multiply H_2SO_3 by 3 and then provide the same number of Cr and S atoms on the right. The equation now reads :

Incomplete : $Cr_2O_7^{2-} + 3H_2SO_3 \rightarrow 3Cr^{3+} + 3HSO_4^-$

(*iv*) Balancing oxygen atoms by adding $4H_2O$ on the right, it reads :

Incomplete : $Cr_2O_7^{2-} + 3H_2SO_3 \rightarrow 2Cr^{3} + 3HSO_4^- + 4H_2O$

(*v*) Balancing hydrogen atoms by adding $5H^+$ on the left, we get the final balanced equation :

Balanced : $Cr_2O_7^{2-} + 3H_2SO_3 + 5H^+ \rightarrow 2Cr^{3+} + 3HSO_4^- + 4H_2O$

Example 3. Write a complete balanced equation for the change.

$$Zn + HNO_3 \rightarrow Zn(NO_3)_2 + N_2O + H_2O$$

In this case oxidation number of N in both HNO_3 and $Zn(NO_3)_2$ is +5 but in N_2O it is +1. Thus from HNO_3 to $Zn(NO_3)_2$ the oxidation number of N does not change but in going from HNO_3 to N_2O it changes from +5 to +1. Such equations are balanced by writing HNO_3 twice in reactants. One of these molecules is related to $Zn(NO_3)_2$ and the other to N_2O as illustrated below :

(*i*) Writing skeleton equation HNO_3 twice with oxidation numbers of zinc and nitrogen.

Oxidation numbers :

Skeleton : $$\overset{0}{Zn} + H\overset{+5}{N}O_3 + HNO_3 \rightarrow \overset{+2}{Zn}(NO_3)_2 + N_2\overset{+1}{O} + H_2O$$
$$\downarrow 2e^- \quad \uparrow 4e^-$$

(*ii*) Oxidation number of Zn changes from 0 to +2 and that of N changes from +5 (in HNO_3) to +1 (in N_2O). The Zn atom in going from 0 to +2 has to lose two electrons indicated as usual by ($\downarrow 2e^-$). The N atom in going from +5 to +1 (in N_2O) is to gain 4 electrons indicated by ($\uparrow 4e^-$).

(*iii*) To balance nitrogen atoms between N_2O and HNO_3 undergoing change in oxidation number of N, multiply HNO_3 by 2 and also $4e^-$ by 2.

$$\overset{0}{Zn} + 2HNO_3 + HNO_3 \rightarrow \overset{+2}{Zn}(NO_3)_2 + N_2O + \overset{+1}{H_2}O$$
$$\downarrow 2e^- \quad \uparrow 2 \times 4e^-$$

(*iv*) To balance the oxidation number change multiply Zn by 4. Then provide the same number of Zn atoms on the right.

$$4Zn + 2HNO_3 + HNO_3 \rightarrow 3Zn(NO_3)_2 + N_2O + H_2O$$

(*v*) This gives 8 NO_3 radicals on the right. To provide the same number of NO_3 radicals on the left, multiply HNO_3 (in which oxidation number of N does not change) by 8.

$$4Zn + 2HNO_3 + 8HNO_3 \rightarrow 4Zn(NO_3)_2 + N_2O + H_2O$$

(*vi*) Balance H-atoms on both sides by multiplying H_2O on the right by 5. This balances the oxygen atoms also.

$$4Zn + 2HNO_3 + 8HNO_3 \rightarrow 4Zn(NO_3)_2 + N_2O + 5H_2O$$

or $$4Zn + 10HNO_3 \rightarrow 4Zn(NO_3)_2 + N_2O + 5H_2O$$

TEST YOUR UNDERSTANDING

1. Fill in the blanks in the following :

(1) Oxidation involves .... of electrons and is, therefore, termed ....

(2) Reduction involves .... of electrons and is, therefore, termed ....

(3) In order to keep track of .... in oxidation-reduction reaction, it is convenient to use the concept of .... or .... of various atoms involved in these reactions.

(4) The oxidation number is defined as the .... which an atom .... when electrons are .... in accordance with the following .... rules.

(*a*) Electrons .... between two unlike atoms are counted with ....

(*b*) Electrons .... between two like atoms are ....

(5) In the elementary or .... state, the atoms are assigned an oxidation number of ....

(6) In compounds, the oxidation number of fluorine is always ....

(7) In compunds, alkali metals (.............) have an oxidation number .... and the group II A elements (.............) have an oxidation number ....

(8) Oxidation number of hydrogen in metal hydrides is .... and in other compounds is ....

(9) Oxidation number of oxygen in F_2O is .... and in all other compounds it is ....

(10) In neutral molecules the sum of oxidation numbers of ....is zero.

(11) In charged species (ions), the sum of the .... of all the atoms is equal to ....

(12) Oxidation state of element is its .... per atom.

(13) Oxidation involves .... in oxidation number while reduction involves .... in oxidation number.

2. Rewrite the following steps involved in the systematic procedure for balacing a chemical equation by oxidation number method :

(*i*) Assign oxidation numbers to ....

(*ii*) Choose the proper ratio of .... to the .... so that the oxidation number change is ....

(*iii*) Make appropriate change in the .... corresponding to the change of .... in step (*ii*).

(*iv*) Balance oxygen atoms by adding .... to the side that is .... in oxygen.

(*v*) Balance hydrogen atoms by adding .... to the side that is .... in hydrogen.

(*vi*) If the reaction is taking place in alkaline solution, add sufficient number of .... to get rid of .... but add number of ...... on both sides.

(*vii*) Cancel .... if any, on both sides of equation.

KEY

1. (1) removal, de-electronation ; (2) addition, electronation ; (3) electron shifts, oxidation number, oxidation state ; (4) formal charge, appears to have, counted, rather arbitrary ;

(*a*) Shared, more electronegative ;

(*b*) shared, divided equally between the two sharing atoms.

(5) uncombined, zero ; (6) –1 ;

(7) (Li, Na, K, Rb, Cs and Fr), +1 ;

(Be, Mg, Ca, Sr, Ba and Ra), +2 ;

(8) –1, +1 ;

(9) +2, –2 ;

(10) all the atoms ; (11) oxidation numbers, the net charge on the ion ;

(12) oxidation number ; (13) increase, decrease.

2. (*i*) the atoms that change ; (*ii*) oxidising agent, reducing agent, balanced.

(*iii*) coefficients of the products, coefficients of reactants ;

(*iv*) H_2O, deficient ; (*v*) H^+, deficient ; (*vii*) OH^-, H^+ OH^-:

(*viii*) duplication.

EXERCISES

1. (*a*) Explain the terms :

(*i*) Oxidation number (*ii*) Oxidation and (*iii*) Valency.

(*b*) What is the oxidation number of the italicized elements in the following :

(*i*) $S_4O_6^{2-}$; (*ii*) RuO_4; (*iii*) K_2TaF_7;

(*iv*) ZnO; (*v*) K_2PtCl_6; (*vi*) Sb_2S_5;

(*vii*) Na_2MoO_8, and (*viii*) $H_2C_2O_4$?

(*c*) What is the oxidation number of the element associated with oxygen in each of the following radical ions ?

(*i*) CrO_4^{2-} (*ii*) PO_4^{3-} (*iii*) CO_3^{2-}

(*iv*) HPO_3^{2-} (*v*) NO_3^- (*vi*) SO_3^{2-}

(*vii*) NO_2, (*viii*) SO_4^{2-} (*ix*) OH^-

(*x*) ClO_3^- (*xi*) ClO_4^- (*xii*) ClO^-

2. Balance the following equations using oxidation numbers :

(*i*) $CH_4 + O_2 \rightarrow CO_2 + H_2O$

(*ii*) $KMnO_4 + C_6H_{12}O_6 \rightarrow MnO + CO_2 + H_2O + K_2CO_3$

(*iii*) $H_2S + NO_3^- \rightarrow NO_2$ in acidic solution

(*iv*) $HS^- + NO_3^- \rightarrow NO_2^-$ in basic solution

(*v*) $Al + OH^- \rightarrow Al(OH)_4^- + H_2$

(*vi*) $SbCl_3 + KIO_3 + HCl \rightarrow SbCl_5 + KI + H_2O$

(*vii*) $AsH_3 + KClO_3 \rightarrow H_3AsO_4 + KCl$

(*viii*) $P + HNO_3 \rightarrow H_3PO_4 + NO$

(*ix*) $KMnO_4 + FeSO_4 + H_2SO_4 \rightarrow K_2SO_4 + MnSO_4 + Fe_2(SO_4)_3 + H_2O$

3. Balance the following equations by the oxidation number method :

(*i*) $C_2H_5OH + O_2 \rightarrow CO_2 + H_2O$

(*ii*) $C_6H_{12}O_6 + H_2SO_4 \rightarrow CO_2 + SO_2 + H_2O$

(*iii*) $C_3H_8O_3 + HNO_3 \rightarrow CO_2 + NO + H_2O$

(*iv*) $S + HNO_3 \rightarrow SO_2 + NO_2 + H_2O$

(*v*) $C_4H_8 + HMnO_4 + H_2SO_4 \rightarrow HC_2H_3O_2 + K_2SO_4 + MnSO_4 + H_2O$

(*vi*) $HCHO + KMnO_4 + HCl \rightarrow MnCl_2 + HCOOH + KCl + H_2$

(*vii*) $C_2H_2 + KMnO_4 \rightarrow MnO_2 + K_2C_2O_4 + KOH + H_2O$

(*viii*) $C_6H_{12}O + K_2Cr_2O_7 + H_2SO_4 \rightarrow C_6H_{10}O + Cr_2(SO_4)_3 + K_2SO_4 + H_2O$

(*ix*) $C_2H_6O + K_2Cr_2O_7 + H_2SO_4 \rightarrow HC_2H_3O_2 + K_2SO_4 + Cr_2(SO_4)_3 + H_2O$

4. Balance the following equations by the oxidation number method :

(1) $Cr_2(SO_4)_3 + KMnO_4 + H_2O \rightarrow H_2Cr_2O_7 + H_2SO_4 + MnSO_4 + K_2SO_4$

(2) $SbCl_3 + KBrO_3 + HCl \rightarrow SbCl_5 + KBr + H_2O$

(3) $SnCl_2 + I_2 + HCl \rightarrow SnCl_4 + HI$

(4) $FeCl_2 + K_2Cr_2O_7 + HCl \rightarrow FeCl_3 + CrCl_3 + KCl + H_2O$

(5) $KI + KIO_3 + HCl \rightarrow I_2 + KCl + H_2O$

(6) $H_2CrO_4 + FeSO_4 + H_2SO_4 \rightarrow Cr_2(SO_4)_3 + Fe_2(SO_4)_3 + H_2O$

(7) $KNO_2 + KI + HCl \rightarrow KCl + I_2 + NO + H_2O$

(8) $CuO + NH_3 \rightarrow Cu + N_2 + H_2O$

(9) $HNO_3 + H_2S \rightarrow NO + H_2SO_4 + H_2O$

(10) $Cu + HNO_3 + HNO_3 \rightarrow C_4(NO_3)_2 + NO + H_2O$

(11) $H_2SO_4 + HI \rightarrow H_2S + H_2O + I_2$

Copper is cleaned by dipping it into nitric acid.

(12) $KI + KIO_3 + H_2SO_4 \rightarrow I_2 + K_2SO_4 + H_2O$

(13) $MnO_2 + FeSO_4 + H_2SO_4 \rightarrow Fe_2(SO_4)_3 + MnSO_4 + H_2O$

(14) $Ce(SO_4)_2 + H_3AsO_3 + H_2O \rightarrow H_3AsO_4 + Ce_2(SO_4)_3 + H_2SO_4$

(15) $H_2S + H_2SO_4 + KMnO_4 \rightarrow K_2SO_4 + MnSO_4 + S + H_2O$

(16) $Cu + HNO_3 + HNO_3 \rightarrow Cu(NO_3)_2 + NO_2 + H_2O$

(17) $Zn + HNO_3 + HNO_3 \rightarrow Zn(NO_3)_2 + NH_4NO_3 + H_2O$

(18) $H_2O_2 + KI + HCl \rightarrow KCl + I_2 + H_2O$

(19) $Ce(SO_4)_2 + H_2O_2 \rightarrow Ce_2(SO_4)_3 + H_2SO_4 + O_2$

(20) $H_2SO_3 + HNO_3 \rightarrow H_2SO_4 + NO + H_2O$

(21) $KMnO_4 + H_3AsO_3 + HCl \rightarrow KCl + MnCl_2 + H_3AsO_4 + H_2O$

ANSWERS

1. (*b*) (*i*) +2 1/2; (*ii*) +8; (*iii*) +5; (*iv*) +2;
(*v*) +4; (*vi*) +5; (*vii*) +14; (*viii*) +3;
(*c*) (*i*) +6; (*ii*) +5; (*iii*) +4; (*iv*) +3;
(*v*) +5; (*vi*) +4; (*vii*) +3; (*viii*) +6;
(*ix*) +1; (*x*) +5; (*xi*) +7; (*xii*) +1.

2. (*i*)
$$\underset{\downarrow 8e^-}{\overset{-4}{C}H_4} + \underset{\uparrow 4e^-}{2\overset{0}{O}_2} \rightarrow \overset{+4}{C}O_2 + 2H_2\overset{-2}{O}$$

(*ii*)
$$\underset{\uparrow 5e^-}{24K\overset{+7}{Mn}O_4} + \underset{\downarrow 24e^-}{5\overset{0}{C}_6H_{12}O_6} \rightarrow 24\overset{+2}{Mn}O + 18\overset{+4}{C}O_2 + 30H_2O + 12K_2\overset{+4}{C}O_3$$

(*iii*)
$$\underset{\downarrow 2e^-}{H_2\overset{-2}{S}} + \underset{\uparrow 2e^-}{2\overset{+5}{N}O_3} + 2H^+ \rightarrow \overset{0}{S} + 2\overset{+4}{N}O_2 + 2H_2O$$

(*iv*)
$$\left.\underset{\downarrow 2e^-}{H\overset{-2}{S}^-} + \underset{\uparrow 2e^-}{\overset{+5}{N}O_3^-} \rightarrow \overset{0}{S} + \overset{+3}{N}O_2^- + OH^- \right\}$$

(*v*)
$$\underset{\downarrow 3e^-}{2\overset{0}{Al}} + 2OH^- + \underset{\uparrow e^-}{6\overset{+1}{H}OH} \rightarrow 2\overset{+3}{Al}(OH)_4^- + 3\overset{0}{H}_2$$

(*vi*)
$$\underset{\downarrow 2e^-}{3\overset{+3}{Sb}Cl_3} + \underset{\uparrow 6e^-}{K\overset{+5}{I}O_3} + 6HCl \rightarrow 3\overset{+5}{Sb}\,Cl_5 + K\overset{-1}{I} + 3H_2O$$

(*vii*)
$$\underset{\downarrow 8e^-}{3\overset{-3}{As}H_3} + \underset{\uparrow +6e^-}{4K\overset{+5}{Cl}O_3} \rightarrow 3H_3\overset{+5}{As}O_4 + 4K\overset{-1}{Cl}$$

(*viii*)
$$\underset{\downarrow 5e^-}{3\overset{0}{P}} + \underset{\uparrow 3e^-}{5H\overset{+5}{N}O_3} + 2H_2O \rightarrow 3H_3\overset{+5}{P}O_4 + 5\overset{+2}{N}O$$

(*ix*)
$$\underset{\uparrow 5e^-}{2K\overset{+7}{Mn}O_4} + \underset{\downarrow e^-}{10\overset{+2}{Fe}SO_4} + 8H_2SO_4 \rightarrow K_2SO_4 + 2\overset{+2}{Mn}SO_4$$
$$+ 5\overset{+6}{Fe}_2(SO_4)_3 + 8H_2O$$

3. (*i*)
$$\underset{\uparrow 12e^-}{C_2H_5OH} + \underset{\uparrow 4e^{o-}}{3\overset{0}{O}_2} \rightarrow 2\overset{+4-4}{CO}_2 + 3H_2\overset{-2}{O}$$

(*ii*)
$$\underset{\downarrow 24e^-}{\overset{0}{C}_6H_{12}\,O_6} + \underset{\uparrow 2e^-}{12H_2\overset{+6}{S}O_4} \rightarrow 6\overset{+4}{C}O_2 + 18H_2O + 12\overset{+4}{S}O_2$$

(*iii*)
$$\underset{\downarrow 14e^-}{3\overset{-2}{C}_3H_8O_3} + \underset{\uparrow 3e^-}{14H\overset{+5}{N}O_3} \rightarrow 9\overset{+4}{C}O_2 + 19H_2O + 14\overset{+2}{N}O$$

(*iv*)
$$\underset{\downarrow 4e^-}{\overset{0}{S}} + \underset{\uparrow e^{-3}}{4H\overset{+5}{N}O_3} \rightarrow \overset{+4}{S}O_2 + 4\overset{+4}{N}O_2 + H_2O$$

(*v*)
$$\underset{\downarrow 8e^-}{5\overset{+8}{C}_4H_8} + \underset{\uparrow 5e^-}{8K\overset{+7}{Mn}O_4} + 12H_2SO_4 \rightarrow 10H\overset{0}{C}_2H_3O_2 + 4K_2SO_4$$
$$+ 8\overset{+2}{Mn}SO_4 + 12H_2O$$

(vi) $$5\underset{\downarrow 2e^-}{\overset{0}{\text{HCHO}}} + 2\underset{\uparrow 5e^-}{\overset{+7}{\text{KMnO}_4}} + 6\text{HCl} \rightarrow 2\overset{+2}{\text{MnCl}_2} + 5\overset{+2}{\text{HCOOH}} + 2\text{KCl} + 3\text{H}_2\text{O}$$

(vii) $$3\underset{\downarrow 8e^-}{\overset{-2}{\text{C}_2\text{H}_2}} + 8\underset{\uparrow 3e^-}{\overset{+7}{\text{KMnO}_4}} \rightarrow 8\overset{+4}{\text{MnO}_2} + 3\overset{+6}{\text{K}_2\text{C}_2\text{O}_4} + 2\text{KOH} + 2\text{H}_2\text{O}$$

(viii) $$3\underset{\downarrow 2e^-}{\overset{-10}{\text{C}_6}}\text{H}_{12}\text{O} + \underset{\uparrow 6e}{\overset{+12}{\text{K}_2\text{Cr}_2\text{O}_7}} + 4\text{H}_2\text{SO}_4 \rightarrow 3\overset{-8}{\text{C}_6}\text{H}_{10}\text{O} + \overset{+6}{\text{Cr}_2}(\text{SO}_4)_3 + \text{K}_2\text{SO}_4 + 7\text{H}_2\text{O}$$

+12

(ix) $$3\underset{\downarrow 4e^-}{\overset{-4}{\text{C}_2\text{H}_6\text{O}}} + 2\underset{\uparrow 6e^-}{\overset{+12}{\text{K}_2\text{Cr}_2\text{O}_7}} + 8\text{H}_2\text{SO}_4 \rightarrow 3\overset{0}{\text{H}}\text{C}_2\text{H}_3\text{O}_2 + 2\text{K}_2\text{SO}_4 + 2\overset{+6}{\text{Cr}_2}(\text{SO}_4)_3 + 11\text{H}_2\text{O}$$

4. (1) $$5\underset{\downarrow 6e^-}{\overset{+6}{\text{Cr}_2}}(\text{SO}_4)_3 + 6\underset{\uparrow 5e^-}{\overset{+7}{\text{KMnO}_4}} + 11\text{H}_2\text{O} \rightarrow 5\overset{+12}{\text{H}_2\text{Cr}_2\text{O}_7} + 3\text{K}_2\text{SO}_4 + 6\text{H}_2\text{SO}_4 + 6\text{MnSO}_4$$

(2) $$3\underset{\downarrow 2e^-}{\overset{+3}{\text{SbCl}_3}} + \underset{\uparrow 6e^-}{\overset{+5}{\text{KBrO}_3}} + 6\text{HCl} \rightarrow 3\overset{+5}{\text{SbCl}_5} + \overset{-1}{\text{KBr}} + 3\text{H}_2\text{O}$$

(3) $$\underset{\downarrow 2e^-}{\overset{+2}{\text{SnCl}_2}} + \underset{\uparrow 2e^-}{\text{I}_2\text{O}} + 2\text{HCl} \rightarrow \overset{+4}{\text{SnCl}_4} + 2\overset{-1}{\text{HI}}$$

(4) $$6\underset{\downarrow e^-}{\overset{+2}{\text{FeCl}_2}} + \underset{\uparrow 6e^-}{\overset{+12}{\text{K}_2\text{Cr}_2\text{O}_7}} + 14\text{HCl} \rightarrow 6\overset{+3}{\text{FeCl}_3} + 2\overset{+3}{\text{CrCl}_3} + 2\text{KCl} + 7\text{H}_2\text{O}$$

(5) $$5\underset{\downarrow e^-}{\overset{-1}{\text{KI}}} + \underset{\uparrow 5e^-}{\overset{+5}{\text{KIO}_3}} + 6\text{HCl} \rightarrow 3\overset{0}{\text{I}_2} + 6\text{KCl} + 3\text{H}_2\text{O}$$

(6) $$2\text{H}_2\underset{\uparrow 3e^-}{\overset{+6}{\text{CrO}_4}} + 6\underset{\downarrow e^-}{\overset{+2}{\text{FeSO}_4}} + 6\text{H}_2\text{SO}_4 \rightarrow \overset{+6}{\text{Cr}_2}(\text{SO}_4)_3 + 3\overset{+6}{\text{Fe}_2}(\text{SO}_4)_3 + 8\text{H}_2\text{O}$$

(7) $$2\underset{\uparrow e^-}{\overset{+3}{\text{KNO}_2}} + 2\underset{\downarrow e^-}{\overset{-1}{\text{KI}}} + 4\text{HCl} \rightarrow 4\text{KCl} + 2\overset{+2}{\text{NO}} + 2\text{H}_2\text{O} + \overset{0}{\text{I}_2}$$

(8) $\underset{\uparrow 2e^-}{3\overset{+2}{Cu}} \rightarrow \underset{\downarrow 3e^-}{2\overset{-3}{N}H_3} \rightarrow \overset{0}{Cu} + \overset{0}{N_2} + 3H_2O$

(9) $\underset{\uparrow 3e^-}{8H\overset{+5}{N}O_3} + \underset{\downarrow 8e^-}{3H_2\overset{-2}{S}} \rightarrow$

$8\overset{+2}{N}O + 3H_2\overset{+6}{S}O_4 + 4H_2O$

(10) $\underset{\downarrow 2e^-}{3\overset{0}{Cu}} + 6HNO_3 + \underset{\uparrow 3e^-}{2H\overset{+5}{N}O_3} \rightarrow$

$3\overset{+2}{Cu}(NO_3)_2 + 2\overset{+2}{N}O + 4H_2O$

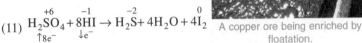

A copper ore being enriched by floatation.

(11) $\underset{\uparrow 8e^-}{H_2\overset{+6}{S}O_4} + \underset{\downarrow e^-}{8H\overset{-1}{I}} \rightarrow H_2\overset{-2}{S} + 4H_2O + 4\overset{0}{I_2}$

(12) $\underset{\downarrow e^-}{5K\overset{-1}{I}} + \underset{\uparrow 5e^-}{K\overset{+5}{I}O_3} + 3H_2SO_4 \rightarrow 3\overset{0}{I_2} + 3K_2SO_4 + 3H_2O$

(13) $\underset{\uparrow 2e^-}{\overset{+4}{Mn}O_2} + \underset{\downarrow e^-}{2\overset{+2}{Fe}SO_4} + 2H_2SO_4 \rightarrow \overset{+6}{Fe_2}(SO_4)_3 + \overset{+2}{Mn}SO_4 + 2H_2O$

(14) $\underset{\uparrow e^-}{2\overset{+4}{Ce}(SO_4)_2} + \underset{\downarrow 2e^-}{H_2\overset{+3}{As}O_3} + H_2O \rightarrow H_3\overset{+5}{As}O_4 + \overset{+6}{Ce_2}(SO_4)_3 + H_2SO_4$

(15) $\underset{\downarrow 2e^-}{5H_2\overset{-2}{S}} + 3H_2SO_4 + \underset{\uparrow 5e^-}{2K\overset{+7}{Mn}O_4} \rightarrow K_2SO_4 + 2\overset{+2}{Mn}SO_4 + 5\underset{+4}{\overset{0}{S}} + 8H_2O$

(16) $\underset{\downarrow 2e^-}{\overset{0}{Cu}} + 2HNO_3 + \underset{\uparrow e^-}{2H\overset{+5}{N}O_3} \rightarrow \overset{+2}{Cu}(NO_3)_2 + 2\overset{+4}{N}O_2 + 2H_2O$

(17) $\underset{\downarrow 2e^-}{4\overset{0}{Zn}} + \underset{\uparrow 8e^-}{9HNO_3} + H\overset{+5}{N}O_3 \rightarrow 4\overset{+2}{Zn}(NO_3)_2 + \overset{-3}{N}H_4NO_3 + 3H_2O$

(18). $\underset{\uparrow 2e^-}{H_2\overset{-2}{O_2}} + \underset{\downarrow e^-}{2K\overset{-1}{I}} + 2HCl \rightarrow 2KCl + \overset{0}{I_2} + 2H_2\overset{-2}{O}$

(19) $\underset{\uparrow e^-}{2\overset{+4}{Ce}(SO_4)_3} + \underset{\downarrow 2e^-}{H_2\overset{-2}{O_2}} \rightarrow \overset{+6}{Ce_2}(SO_4)_3 + H_2SO_4 + \overset{0}{O_2}$

(20) $\underset{\downarrow 2e^-}{3H_2\overset{+4}{S}O_3} + \underset{\uparrow 3e^-}{2H\overset{+5}{N}O_2} \rightarrow 3H_2\overset{+6}{S}O_4 + 2\overset{+2}{N}O + H_2O$

(21) $\underset{\uparrow 5e^-}{2K\overset{+7}{Mn}O_4} + \underset{\downarrow 2e^-}{5H_3\overset{+3}{As}O_3} + 6HCl \rightarrow 2KCl + 2\overset{+2}{Mn}Cl_2$

$+ 5H_3\overset{+5}{As}O_4 + 3H_2O$

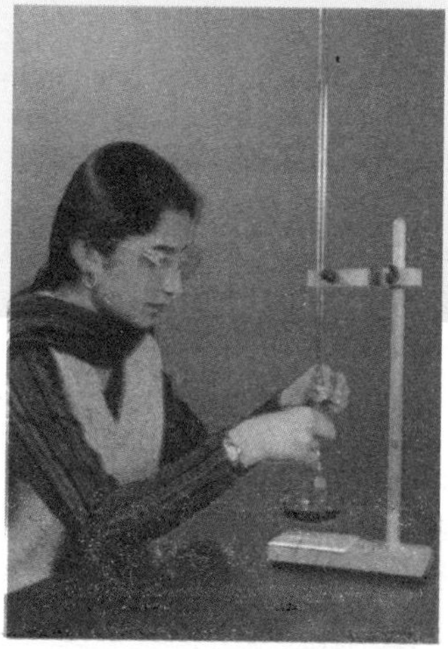

7
CHAPTER

Test Yourself on These Typical Questions-I

1. Write complete equations for the following reactions :

(*i*) Magnesium + Nitrogen → Magnesium nitride :

(*ii*) Ammonium nitrite → Nitrogen + Water.

(*iii*) Sulphur + Sulphuric acid → Sulphur dioxide + Water.

(*iv*) Iodic acid + Hydriodic acid → Iodine + Water.

(*v*) Iron pyrites + Oxygen → Ferric oxide + Sulphurous anhydride.

Iron pyrite, FeS_2 (also known as fool's gold).

(*vi*) Calcium phosphide + Water → Calcium hydroxide + Phosphine.

(*vii*) Copper + Nitric acid → Copper nitrate + Nitrogen dioxide + Water

2. Explain what happens when
   (i) a piece of burning magnesium is lowered in a gas jar containing carbon dioxide.
   (ii) carbon dioxide is passed through lime water for a long time and the resulting solution is boiled.
   (iii) bromine reacts with (a) hot soluton of caustic potash, (b) hydrogen sulphide, (c) sulphurous acid, (d) potassium iodide solution.
   (iv) concentrated hydrochloric acid is added to potassium premanganate.
3. Balance the following equations :
   (i) $NaCl + MnO_2 + H_2SO_4 \rightarrow NaHSO_4 + MnSO_4 + H_2O + Cl_2$

Soduim chloride is the principal source of the reactive metal sodium. Most NaCl is mined.

   (ii) $FeSO_4 + H_2SO_4 + Cl_2 \rightarrow Fe_2(SO_4)_3 + HCl$
   (iii) $Zn + HNO_3 \rightarrow Zn(NO_3)_2 + N_2O + H_2O$
   (iv) $K_2Cr_2O_7 + H_2SO_4 + SO_2 \rightarrow K_2SO_4 + Cr_2(SO_4)_3 + H_2O$
   (v) $Fe_2(SO_4)_3 + SO_2 + H_2O \rightarrow FeSO_4 + H_2SO_4$
   (vi) $KMnO_4 + H_2SO_4 + H_2S \rightarrow K_2SO_4 + MnSO_4 + H_2O + S$
4. Balance the following equations :
   (i) $Zn + HNO_3 \rightarrow Zn(NO_3)_2 + NO_2 + H_2O$
   (ii) $Fe_2(SO_4)_3 + SO_2 + H_2O \rightarrow FeSO_4 + H_2SO_4$
   (iii) $I_2 + HNO_3 \rightarrow HIO_3 + NO_2 + H_2O$
   (iv) $P + HNO_3 \rightarrow H_3PO_4 + NO_2 + H_2O$
   (v) $As_2O_3 + HCl + SnCl_2 \rightarrow As + SnCl_4 + H_2O$
5. Explain, giving equations, what happens when–
   (a) Burning magnesium is introduced into a jar of carbon dioxide.
   (b) Hydrogen sulphide is passed through an acidified solution of copper sulphate.
   (c) A mixture of sodium chloride and manganese dioxide is heated with concentrated sulphuric acid.

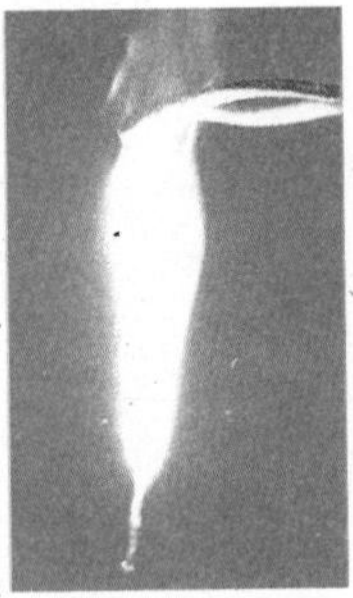

Magnesium burns with a brilliant white flame.

(*d*) Chlorine is passed through a solution of sodium hydroxide.
(*e*) Phosphorus is heated with caustic potash.

6. Give equations and names of products formed for the reactions which take place in the following cases :
(*a*) Potassium permanganate is heated.
(*b*) Mercuric chloride reacts with stannous chloride.
(*c*) Iodine reacts with sodium thiosulphate.
(*d*) Hydrochloric acid reacts with tin metal.
(*e*) Phosphine is passed through a solution of copper sulphate.
(*f*) Carbon monoxide is passed over heated caustic soda, under pressure.
(*g*) Oxalic acid is heated with conc. sulphuric acid.
(*h*) Bromine reacts with caustic potash solution.

7. Give equations and names of products formed for the reactions which take place in the following cases :
(*a*) Carbon dioxide is passed through lime water.
(*b*) Sulphur is heated with concentrated nitric acid.
(*c*) Hydrogen sulphide is passed through ammoniacal solution of zinc sulphate.
(*d*) Iodine reacts with sodium thiosulphate.
(*e*) Chlorine reacts with slaked lime.
(*f*) Sulphur vapours are passed over red hot coke.
(*g*) Phosphorus pentoxide reacts with concentrated nitric acid.
(*h*) Nitric oxide reacts with ferrous sulphate solution.

At room temperature and atmospheric pressure, chlorine is a pale green gas, bromine an orange liquid and iodine a dark purple solid.

8. Complete and balance the following equations :

(*i*) $HNO_2 = HNO_3 + NO +$ ....

(*ii*) $NH_3 + NaOCl = N_2 + NaCl +$ ....

(*iii*) $Mn_3O_4 + HCl = MnCl_2 + H_2O +$ ....

(*iv*) $As_2S_3 + K_2Cr_2O_7 + H_2SO_4 = H_3AsO_4 + S +$ .... + ...

(*v*) $PbSO_4 + PbS = Pb +$ ....

9. Complete and balance the following equations :

(*i*) $FeSO_4 + H_2SO_4 + HNO_3 = Fe_2(SO_4)_3 +$ .... $+ H_2O$

(*ii*) $Cl_2 + H_2O + HgO = HgCl_2.HgO +$ ....

(*iii*) $P_4 + I_2 + H_2O = H_3PO_4 +$ ....

(*iv*) $CaOCl_2 + NaI + HCl = CaCl_2 + H_2O + NaCl +$ ....

ANSWERS

While answering the questions–what happens when–students will explain each reaction in words and write the chemical equations in addition.

1. (*i*) $3Mg + N_2 \rightarrow Mg_3N_2$

(*ii*) $NH_4NO_2 \rightarrow N_2 + 2H_2O$

(*iii*) $S + 2H_2SO_4 \rightarrow 2SO_2 + 2H_2O$

(*iv*) $HIO_3 + 5HI \rightarrow 3I_2 + 3H_2O$

(*v*) $4FeS_2 + 11O_2 \rightarrow 2Fe_2O_3 + 8SO_2$

(*vi*) $Ca_3P_2 + 6H_2O \rightarrow 3Ca(OH)_2 + 2PH_3$

(*vii*) $Cu + 4HNO_3 \rightarrow Cu(NO_3)_2 + 2NO_2 + 2H_2O$

2. (*i*) $CO_2 + 2Mg \rightarrow C + 2MgO$

(*ii*) $$\underset{\text{Lime water}}{Ca(OH)_2} \xrightarrow[-H_2O]{+CO_2} \underset{\text{Insoluble (Milkiness)}}{CaCO_3} \xrightarrow[+H_2O]{+CO_2} \underset{\text{Soluble (Clearsolution)}}{Ca(HCO_3)_2}$$

$$Ca(HCO_3)_2 \xrightarrow{\text{Boil}} \underset{\text{(Milkiness)}}{CaCO_3} + CO_2 + H_2O$$

(*iii*) (*a*) $6KOH + 3Br_2 \rightarrow KBrO_3 + 5KBr + 3H_2O$

(*b*) $H_2S + Br_2 \rightarrow 2HBr + S$

(*c*) $H_2SO_3 + Br_2 + H_2O \rightarrow H_2SO_4 + 2HBr$

(*d*) $2KI + Br_2 \rightarrow 2KBr + I_2$

(*iv*) $2KMnO_4 + 6HCl \rightarrow 2KCl + 2MnCl_2 + 3H_2O + 5O$

$2HCl + O \rightarrow Cl_2 + H_2O] \times 5$

$2KMnO_4 + 16HCl \rightarrow 2KCl + 2MnCl_2 + 8H_2O + 5Cl_2$

3.(*i*) $NaCl + H_2SO_4 \rightarrow NaHSO_4 + HCl] \times 2$

$MnO_2 + H_2SO_4 \rightarrow MnSO_4 + H_2O + O$

$2HCl + O \rightarrow Cl_2 + H_2O$

$2NaCl + MnO_2 + 3H_2SO_4 \rightarrow 2NaHSO_4 + MnSO_4 + 2H_2O + Cl_2$

(*ii*) $2FeSO_4 + H_2SO_4 + Cl_2 \rightarrow Fe_2(SO_4)_3 + 2HCl$

(*iii*) $4Zn(NO_3)_2 + 10HNO_3 \rightarrow 4Zn(NO_3)_2 + N_2O + 5H_2O$

(iv) $K_2Cr_2O_7 + H_2SO_4 + 3SO_2 \rightarrow K_2SO_4 + Cr_2(SO_4)_3 + H_2O$

(v) $Fe_2(SO_4)_3 + SO_2 + 2H_2O \rightarrow 2FeSO_4 + 2H_2SO_4$

(vi) $2KMnO_4 + 3H_2SO_4 + 5H_2S \rightarrow K_2SO_4 + 2MnSO_4 + 8H_2O + 5S$

4. (i) $Zn + 4HNO_3 \rightarrow Zn(NO_3)_2 + 2NO_2 + 2H_2O$

(ii) $Fe_2(SO_4)_3 + SO_2 + 2H_2O \rightarrow 2FeSO_4 + 2H_2SO_4$

(iii) $I_2 + 10HNO_3 \rightarrow 2HIO_3 + 10NO_2 + 4H_2O$

(iv) $2P + 10HNO_3 \rightarrow 2H_3PO_4 + 10NO_2 + 2H_2O$

(v) $As_2O_3 + 6HCl + 3SnCl_2 \rightarrow 2AS + 3SnCl_4 + 3H_2O$

5. (a) $2Mg + CO_2 \rightarrow 2MgO + C$

(b) $CuSO_4 + H_2S \rightarrow CuS \downarrow + H_2SO_4$

(c) See Q. 3(i)

(d) (i) **In cold :** $2NaOH + Cl_2 \rightarrow NaCl + NaClO + H_2O$

(ii) **In hot :**

$$\begin{array}{l} 2NaOH + Cl_2 \rightarrow NaCl + NaClO + H_2O] \times 3 \\ \quad 3NaClO \rightarrow NaClO_3 + 2NaCl \\ \hline 6NaOH + 3Cl_2 \rightarrow NaClO_3 + 5NaCl + 3H_2O \end{array}$$

(e) $P_4 + 3NaOH + 3H_2O \rightarrow PH_3 + 3NaH_2PO_2$

6. (a) $2KMnO_4 \rightarrow K_2MnO_4 + MnO_2 + O_2$

(b) $2HgCl_2 + SnCl_2 \rightarrow Hg_2Cl_2 + SnCl_4$

$Hg_2Cl_2 + SnCl_2 \rightarrow 2Hg + SnCl_4$

(c) $2Na_2S_2O_3 + I_2 \rightarrow Na_2S_4O_6 + 2NaI$

(d) $Sn + 2HCl \rightarrow SnCl_2 + H_2$

(e) $3CuSO_4 + 2PH_3 \rightarrow \underset{\text{copper phosphide}}{Cu_3P_2} + 3H_2SO_4$

(f) $NaOH + CO \rightarrow \underset{\text{Sod. formate}}{HCOONa}$

(g) $(COOH)_2 + H_2SO_4 \rightarrow CO + CO_2 + [H_2SO_4.H_2O]$

(h) (i) **In cold :**

$Br_2 + 2KOH \rightarrow KBr + KBrO + H_2O$

(ii) **On heating :**

$$\begin{array}{l} Br_2 + 2KOH \rightarrow KBr + KBrO + H_2O] \times 3 \\ \quad 3KBrO \rightarrow KBrO_3 + 2KBr \\ \hline Br_2 + 6KOH \rightarrow 5KBr + KBrO_3 + 3H_2O \end{array}$$

7. (*a*) See Ans. 2(*i*)

(*b*) $2HNO_3 \rightarrow 2NO_2 + H_2O + O] \times 3$

$$S + 3O + H_2O \rightarrow H_2SO_4$$

$$\overline{S + 6HNO_3 \rightarrow H_2SO_4 + 6NO_2 + 2H_2O + NH_4OH}$$

(*c*) $ZnSO_4 + H_2S \rightarrow ZnS + H_2SO_4$

$H_2SO_4 + 2NH_4OH \rightarrow (NH_4)_2SO_4 + 2H_2O$

(*d*) $2Na_2S_2O_3 + I_3 \rightarrow Na_2S_4O_6 + 2NaI$

(*e*) $Ca(OH)_2 + Cl_2 \rightarrow CaOCl_2 + H_2O$

(*f*) $C + 2S \rightarrow CS_2$

(*g*) $4HNO_3 + P_4O_{10} \rightarrow 2N_2O_5 + 4HPO_3$

(*h*) $FeSO_4 + NO \rightarrow FeSO_4.NO$

nitroso-ferrous sulphate
(dark brown compound)

8. (*i*) $3HNO_2 = HNO_3 + 3NO + H_2O$

(*ii*) $2NH_3 + 3NaOCl = N_2 + 3NaCl + 3H_2O$

(*iii*) $Mn_3O_4 + 8HCl = 3MnCl_2 + H_2O + Cl_2$

(*iv*) $K_2Cr_2O_7 + 4H_2SO_4 \rightarrow K_2SO_4 + Cr_2(SO_4)_3 + 4H_2O + 3O] \times 5$

$$As_2S_3 + 5O + 3H_2O \rightarrow 2H_3AsO_4 + 3S] \times 3$$

$$\overline{5K_2Cr_2O_7 + 20H_2SO_4 + 3As_2S_3 \rightarrow 6H_3AsO_4 + 9S + 5K_2SO_4}$$

$$+ 5Cr_2(SO_4)_3 + 11H_2O$$

(*v*) $PbSO_4 + PbS = 2Pb + 2SO_2$

9. (*i*) $5FeSO_4 + 3H_2SO_4 + 2HNO_3 = 3Fe_2(SO_4)_3 + 2NO + 4H_2O$

(*ii*) $2Cl_2 + H_2O + 2HgO = HgCl_2.HgO + 2HClO$

(*iii*) $P_4 + 10I_2 + 16H_2O = 4H_3PO_4 + 20HI$

(*iv*) $CaOCl_2 + 2NaI + 2HCl = CaCl_2 + H_2O + 2NaCl + I_2$

8 CHAPTER

Test Yourself on These Typical Questions–II

1. Find out the oxidation number of :

(*a*) (*i*) Mn in $KMnO_4$ and K_2MnO_4.

(*ii*) S in $Na_2S_2O_3$ and $N_2S_4O_6$

(*iii*) Cl in $HClO$ and $HClO_2$.

(*b*) (*i*) Cr in $K_2Cr_2O_7, K_2CrO_4, CrO_2Cl_2$ and $CrCl_2$

(*ii*) Cl in $HClO_3$ and $KClO_4$.

(*iii*) P in $NaHPO_2$ and Na_3PO_3.

(*iv*) Mn in $HMnO_4$ and K_2MnO_4.

2. What is the oxidation number of the following :

(*i*) Mn in $KMnO_4$

(*ii*) Cr in $K_2Cr_2O_7$

(*iii*) I in KIO_4

(*iv*) Fe in $K_3Fe(CN)_6$

(v) Fe in $K_4Fe(CN)_6$ (vi) I in HIO_2

(vii) Cl in Cl_2O (viii) O in H_2O

(ix) O in OF_2 (x) S in H_2S

3. Classify the following reactions into two categories 'Oxidation' and 'Reduction' :

(i) $MnO_4^- \longrightarrow MnO_4^{2-}$ (ii) $MnO_4^- \longrightarrow MnO_2$

(iii) $IO^- \longrightarrow IO_3$ (iv) $Cl^- \longrightarrow Cl_2$

(v) $Cr_2O_7^{2-} \longrightarrow CrO_4^{2-}$ (vi) $Cu \longrightarrow Cu^{2+}$

(vii) $H_2S \longrightarrow S$

4. Name one compound each in which the oxidation number of :

(a) Oxygen, is, +2, (b) Hydrogen, is, –1,
(c) Hydrogen, is, +1, (d) Oxygen, is, –2,
(e) Manganese, is, +4, (f) Chlorine, is, +7,
(g) Phosphorus, is, +5, (h) Nitrogen, is, +1,
(i) Oxygen, is, –1, (j) Nitrogen, is –3.

5. What are various common oxidation states of manganese and chlorine? Give one example of each of these compounds.

6. What do you understand by formal charge ? Calculate the formal charge in the following cases :

(i) Nitrogen in NH_3, NH_4^{+1} and NH_2^-;

(ii) Chlorine in $HClO_2$, $HClO_3$ and $HClO_4^-$;

(iii) Carbon in CH_3^+, CH_3^- and CH_3;

(iv) Sulphur in H_2SO_4;

(v) Phosphorus in H_3PO_4;

(vi) Silicon in SiF_6^{2-}

White phosphorus sponteneously inflames in oxygen, yielding an incandescent white smoke of solid p_4O_{10}.

7. In the ionic equation

$$MnO_4^- + C_2O_4^{2-} \longrightarrow 2CO_2 + Mn^{2+} \quad \textit{(in acidic solution)}$$

(i) Name the reducing agent.
(ii) Separate this into two balanced half-reactions.
(iii) What is the change in oxidation number of Mn ?

8. In the redox reaction equation

$$[Fe(CN)_6]^{4-} + H_2O_2 \xrightarrow[\text{medium}]{\text{acidic}} [Fe(CN)_6]^{3-}$$

(*i*) Give change in oxidation number of Fe.
(*ii*) Point out the element undergoing reduction.
(*iii*) Give two balanced half-reactions.
(*iv*) Write down complete and balanced equation on the basis of ion-electron method.

9. Complete and balance the following equations by ion-electron method:

(*i*) $AsO_3^{3-} + I_2 + H_2O \rightarrow AsO_4^{3-} + H^+ + I^-$

(*ii*) $Cr_2O_7^{2-} + H^+ + I^- \rightarrow Cr^{3+} + H_2O + I_2$

(*iii*) $NO_3^- + I^- + H^+ \rightarrow NO + I_2 + H_2O$

(*iv*) $MnO_4^- + H_2O_2 + H^+ \rightarrow H_2O + O_2 + \ldots$

10. Identify the oxidant and the reductant in the following redox reactions. Also show the change of the oxidation state of the involved atoms.

(*i*) $Cr_2O_7^{2-} + 3SO_3^{2-} + 8H+ \rightarrow 2Cr^{3+} + 3SO_4^{2-} + 4H_2O$

(*ii*) $2NO_3^- + 3CuS + 8H+ \rightarrow 3Cu^{2+} + 2NO + 3S + 2H_2O$

11. Complete and balance the following by ion-electron method :

(*i*) $Cu + NO_3^-$ (in acid) $\rightarrow Cu^{2+} + NO_2$

(*ii*) $KMnO_4 + H_2S$ (in acid) $\rightarrow Mn^{2+} + K^+ + S + H_2O$

(*iii*) $MnO_4^- + Cl^-$ (in acid) $\rightarrow Mn^{2+} + Cl_2 + H_2O$

(*iv*) $Kr_2Cr_2O_7 + SO_2$ (in acid) $\rightarrow Cr^{3+} + K^+ + H_2SO_4 + H_2O$

12. Write net ionic equations for the following reactions :

1. $NaOH(aq) + H_2SO_4(aq) \rightarrow$
2. $Fe(OH)_3(s) + HCl(aq) \rightarrow$
3. $Na_3PO_4(aq) + Pb(NO_3)_2(aq) \rightarrow$
4. $BaCl_2(aq) + Na_2SO_4(aq) \rightarrow$
5. $HCl(aq) + CaCO_3(s) \rightarrow$
6. $BaO(s) + H_2SO_4(aq) \rightarrow$
7. $Ca(s) + H_2O(l) \rightarrow$
8. $Ni(NO_3)_3(aq) + KOH(aq) \rightarrow$
9. $ZnSO_4(aq) + (NH_4)_2S(aq) \rightarrow$

Limestone is mainly calcium carbonate ($CaCO_3$).

13. Balance the following equations by the oxidation number method :

(*i*) $HI + H_2SO_4 \rightarrow H_2S + H_2O + I_2$

(*ii*) $H_2SO_4 + HBr \rightarrow SO_2 + Br_2 + H_2O$

(*iii*) $MnO_2 + HCl \rightarrow MnCl_2 + Cl_2 + H_2O$

(*iv*) $NaNO_3 + Fe \rightarrow Fe_2O_3 + NaNO_2$

(*v*) $CuO + NH_3 \rightarrow Cu + N_2 + H_2O$

(*vi*) $As_4 + HNO_3 + H_2O \rightarrow H_3AsO_4 + NO$

(*vii*) $H_2O_2 + H_2S \rightarrow S + H_2O$

(*viii*) $Mo_2O_3 + KMnO_4 + H_2SO_4 \rightarrow MoO_3 + K_2SO_4 + MnSO_4 + H_2O$

(*ix*) $V_2O_2 + H_2SO_4 + KMnO_4 \rightarrow V_2O_5 + MnSO_4 + K_2SO_4 + H_2O$

(*x*) $AuCl_3 + H_2S + H_2O \rightarrow Au_8 + HCl + H_2SO_4$

14. Write the balanced partial and overall ionic equations for the following redox reactions in the aqueous solution :

(*i*) $Pb^{2+} + Cl_2 + OH^- = PbO_2 + Cl^-$

(*ii*) $Cr_2O_7^{2-} + Fe^{2+} + H^+ = Cr^{3+} + Fe^{3+}$

(*iii*) $MnO_4^{2-} + CO_2 = CO_3^{2-} + MnO_2 + MnO_4^-$

15. (*a*) What do you understand by the term oxidation number ? What rules and conventions are used in denoting oxidation number of various elements ?

(*b*) Calculate the oxidation number of

(*i*) P in HPO_3^{2-}

(*ii*) C in $C_{12}H_{22}O_{11}$

(*iii*) S in $Na_2S_2O_3$

(*iv*) Cr in $Cr_2O_7^{2-}$

16. (*a*) Explain the concept of oxidation number.

(*b*) What are the oxidation numbers of__

(*i*) Mn in $KMnO_4$ and (*ii*) Cr in $Cr_2O_7^{2-}$?

(*c*) In the reaction,

$$SnCl_2 + 2HgCl_2 \longrightarrow SnCl_4 + Hg_2Cl_2$$

mention the oxidising and reducing agents on the basis of oxidation number.

ANSWERS

1. (*a*) (*i*) +7, +6; (*ii*) +2, $2\frac{1}{2}$; (*iii*) +1, +3;
(*b*) (*i*) +6, +6, +6, +2; (*ii*) +5, +7; (*iii*) +2, +3;
(*iv*) +7, +6

2. (*i*) +7, (*ii*) +6; (*iii*) +7;
(*iv*) +3; (*v*) +2; (*vi*) +3;
(*vii*) +1; (*viii*) –2; (*ix*) +2;
(*x*) –2

3. (*i*), (*ii*), involve reduction.
(*iii*), (*iv*), (*vi*), (*vii*) involve oxidation.
(*v*) involves neither reduction nor oxidation.

4. (*a*) OF_4; (*b*) NaH; (*c*) HCl;
(*d*) Na_2O; (*e*) MnO_2; (*f*) $HClO_4$;
(*g*) H_3PO_4; (*h*) N_2O;
(*i*) $H_2O_2 H:O:O:H$ (*j*) NH_3

5. *Manganese* . +2 (in $MnCl_2$), +3 (in Mn_2O_3),

+4 (in MnO_2), +6 (in MnO_4^{2-}) and +7 (in MnO_4^-)

Chlorine : –1 (in HCl), +1 (in HClO), +3 (in $HClO_2$).
+4 (in ClO_2) +5 (in $HClO_3$), +6 (in Cl_2O_6), +7 (in $HClO_4$)

6. Formal charge is the charge which an atom appears to have when electrons are counted in accordance with certain rather arbitrary rules.

(*i*) –3, – 3, – 3; (*ii*) +3, + 5, + 7; (*iii*) –2, – 4, – 3;
(*iv*) +6; (*v*) +5; (*vi*) +4.

7. (*i*) $C_2O_4^{2-}$ is the reducing agent.

(*ii*) $MnO_4^- + 8H^+ + 5e^- \rightarrow Mn^{2+} + 4H_2O$

$$C_2O_4^{2-} \rightarrow 2CO_2 + 2e^-$$

(*iii*) +7 to +2.

8. (*i*) +2 to +3; (*ii*) O in H_2O_2;

(*iii*) $[Fe(CN)_6]^{4-} \rightarrow [Fe(CN)_6[^{2-} + e^-] \times 2$

(*iv*) $$H_2O_2 + 2H^+ + 2e \rightarrow 2H_2O$$

$$2[Fe(CN)_6]^{4-} + H_2O_2 + 2H^+ \rightarrow [Fe(CN)_6]^{3-} + 2H_2O$$

9. *(i)* $AsO_3^{3-} + H_2O \rightarrow AsO_4^{3-} + 2H^+ + 2e^-$

$$I_2 + 2e^- \rightarrow 2I^-$$

$$AsO_3^{3-} + I_2 + H_2O \rightarrow AsO_4^{3-} + 2H^+ + 2I^-$$

(ii) $Cr_2O_7^{2-} + 14H^+ + 6e^- \rightarrow 2Cr^{3+} + 7H_2O$

$$2I^- \rightarrow I_2 + 2e^-] \times 3$$

$$Cr_2O_7^{2-} + 14H^+ + 6I^- \rightarrow 2Cr^{3+} + 7H_2O + 3I_2$$

(iii) $NO_3^- + 4H^+ + 3e^- \rightarrow NO + 2H_2O] \times 2$

$$2I^- \rightarrow I_2 + 2e^-] \times 3$$

$$2NO_3^- + 8H^+ + 6I^- \rightarrow 2NO + 4H_2O + 3I_2$$

(iv) $MnO_4^- + 8H^+ + 5e^- \rightarrow Mn^{2+} + 4H_2O] \times 2$

$$H_2O_2 \rightarrow 2H^+ + O_2 + 2e^-] \times 5$$

$$2MnO_4^- + 6H^+ + 5H_2O_2 \rightarrow 2Mn^{2+} + 8H_2O + 5O_2$$

10. *(i)* Oxidant is $Cr_2O_7^{2-}$ and Reductant is SO_3^{2-} Oxidation number or Cr decreases from $+6$ (in Cr_2O_7) to +3 (in Cr^{3+}) Oxidation number of S increases from $+4$ (in SO_3^{2-}) to $+6$ (in SO_4^{2-}).

(ii) Oxidant is NO_3^- and Reductant is CuS. Oxidation number of N decreases from +5 (in NO_3^-) to +2 (in NO).

Oxidation number of S increases from –2 (in CuS) to 0 (in S).

11. *(i)* $Cu \rightarrow Cu^{2+} + 2e^-$

$$NO_3^- + 2H^+ + e^- \rightarrow NO_2 + H_2O] \times 2$$

$$Cu + 2NO_3^- + 4H^+ \rightarrow Cu^{2+} + 2NO_2 + 2H_2O$$

(ii) $MnO_4^- + 8H^+ + 5e^- \rightarrow Mn^{2+} + 4H_2O] \times 2$

$$H_2S \rightarrow S + 2H^+ + 2e^-] \times 5$$

$$2MnO_4^- + 6H^+ + 5H_2S \rightarrow 2Mn^{2+} + 8H_2O + 5S$$

(*iii*) $MnO_4^+ + 8H^- + 5e^- \rightarrow Mn^{2+} + 4H_2O] \times 2$

$$2Cl^- \rightarrow Cl_2 + 2e^-] \times 5$$

$$\overline{2MnO_4^- + 16H^+ + 10Cl^- \rightarrow 2Mn^{2+} + 8H_2O + 5Cl_2}$$

(*iv*) $Cr_2O_7^{2-} + 14H^+ + 6e^- \rightarrow 2Cr^{3+} + 7H_2O$

$$SO_2 + 2H_2O \rightarrow SO_4^{2-} + 4H^+ + 2e^-] \times 3$$

$$\overline{Cr_2O_7^{2-} + 2H^+ + 3SO_2 \rightarrow 2Cr^{3+} + H_2O + 3SO_4^{2-}}$$

12.

1. $OH^- + H^+ \rightarrow H_2O$
2. $Fe(OH)_3 + 3H^+ \rightarrow Fe^{3+} + 3H_2O$
3. $2PO_4^{3-} + 3Pb^{2+} \rightarrow Pb_3(PO_4)_2 \downarrow$
4. $Cu^{2+} + H_2S \rightarrow CuS \downarrow + 2H^+$
5. $Ba^{2+} + SO_4^{2-} \rightarrow BaSO_4 \downarrow$
6. $2H^+ + CaCO_3 \rightarrow Ca^{2+} + CO_2 + H_2O$
7. $BaO + 2H^+ + SO_4^{2-} \rightarrow BaSO_4 \downarrow + H_2O$
8. $Ca + 2H_2O \rightarrow Ca^{2+} + 2OH^- + H_2$
9. $Ni^{2+} + 20H^- \rightarrow Ni(OH)_2$
10. $Zn^{2+} + S^{2-} \rightarrow ZnS \downarrow$

The vapour pressure of HCl (g) over HCl (Conc.) is considerable. The gaseous HCl molecules react with H_2O molecules is humid air to form a white cloud of hydrochloric acid vapour.

13. (*i*) $$\underset{\downarrow e^-}{8\overset{-1}{H}I} + \underset{\uparrow 8e^-}{H_2\overset{+6}{S}O_4} \rightarrow H_2\overset{-2}{S} + 4\overset{0}{I_2} + 4H_2O$$

(*ii*) $$\underset{\uparrow 2e^-}{H_2\overset{+6}{S}O_4} + \underset{\downarrow e^-}{2H\overset{-1}{Br}} \rightarrow \overset{+4}{S}O_2 + \overset{0}{Br_2} + 2H_2O$$

(*iii*) $$\underset{\uparrow 2e^-}{\overset{+4}{Mn}O_2} + 2H\overset{-1}{Cl} + \underset{\downarrow e^-}{2H\overset{-1}{Cl}} \rightarrow \overset{+2\,-1}{MnCl_2} + \overset{0}{Cl_2} + 2H_2O$$

or $$MnO_2 + 4HCl \rightarrow \underset{+3}{MnCl_2} + Cl_2 + 2H_2O$$

(*iv*) $$\underset{\uparrow 2e^-}{3Na\overset{+5}{N}O_3} + \underset{\downarrow 3e^-}{2\overset{0}{Fe}} \rightarrow \overset{+3}{Fe_2}\,O_3 + 3NaNO_2$$

(v) $$\underset{\uparrow 2e^-}{3\overset{+2}{Cu}O} + \underset{\downarrow 3e^-}{2\overset{-3}{N}H_3} \rightarrow 3\overset{0}{Cu} + \overset{0}{N_2} + 3H_2O$$

(vi) $$\underset{\downarrow 20e^-}{3\overset{0}{As_4}} + \underset{\uparrow 3e^-}{20H\overset{+5}{N}O_3} + 5O_3 + 8H_2O \rightarrow 12H_3\overset{+5}{As}O_4 + 20\overset{+2}{N}O$$

(vii) $$\underset{\uparrow 2e^-}{H_2\overset{-2}{O_2}} + \underset{\downarrow 2e^-}{H_2\overset{-2}{S}} \rightarrow \overset{0}{S} + 2H_2\overset{-2}{O}$$

(viii) $$\underset{\downarrow 6e^-}{5\overset{+3}{Mo_2}O_3} + \underset{\uparrow 5e^-}{6K\overset{+7}{Mn}O_4} + 9H_2SO_4 \rightarrow 10\overset{+6}{Mo}O_3 + 3K_2SO_4$$
$$+ 6\overset{+2}{Mn}SO_4 + 9H_2O$$

(ix) $$\underset{\downarrow 6e^-}{5\overset{+4}{V_2}O_2} + 9H_2SO_4 + \underset{\uparrow 5e^-}{6K\overset{+7}{Mn}O_4} \rightarrow 5\overset{+10}{V_2}O_5 + 6\overset{+2}{Mn}SO_4$$
$$+ 3K_2SO_4 + 9H_2O$$

(x) $$\underset{\uparrow 3e^-}{8\overset{+3}{Au}Cl_3} + \underset{\downarrow 8e^-}{3H_2\overset{-2}{S}} + 12H_2O \rightarrow 8\overset{0}{Au} + 24HCl + 3H_2\overset{+6}{S}O_4$$

14. (*i*) $$Pb^{2+} + 2H_2O + 4OH^- \rightarrow PbO_2 + 4H^+ + 2e^- + 4OH^-$$
$$Cl_2 + 2e^- \rightarrow 2Cl^-$$
$$\overline{\quad Pb^{2+} + Cl_2 + 4OH^- \rightarrow PbO_2 + 2Cl^- + 2H_2O \quad}$$

(*ii*) $$Cr_2O_7^{2-} + 14H^+ + 6e^- \rightarrow 2Cr^{3+} + 7H_2O$$
$$Fe^{2+} \rightarrow Fe^{3+} + e^-] \times 6$$
$$\overline{\quad Cr_2O_7^{2-} + 6Fe^{2+} + 14H^+ \rightarrow 2Cr^{3+} + 6Fe^{3+} + 7H_2O \quad}$$

(*iii*) $$MnO_4^{2-} \rightarrow MnO_4^- + e^-] \times 2$$
$$MnO_4^{2-} + 4H^+ + 2e^- \rightarrow MnO_2 + 2H_2O$$
$$CO_2 + H_2O \rightarrow CO_3^{2-} + 2H^+$$
$$\overline{\quad 3MnO_4^{2-} + CO_2 + 2H^+ \rightarrow 2MnO_4^- + MnO_2 + CO_3^{2-} + H_2O \quad}$$

15. (*b*) (*i*) +3 ; (*ii*) 0 ; (*iii*) +2 ; (*iv*) +6.

16. (*b*) (*i*) +7 ; (*ii*) +6.

(*c*) $SnCl_2$ is the reducing agent wherein oxidation number of Sn increases from $+2(SnCl_2)$ to $+4(\text{in } SnCl_4)$.

$HgCl_2$ is the oxidising agent wherein oxidation number of Hg decreases from $+2(\text{in } HgCl_2)$ to $+1(\text{in } Hg_2Cl_2)$.